ATLAS OF THE MOON

Vincent de Callataÿ

ATLAS
OF THE
MOON

astronomy - astronautics

Translated by R. G. Lascelles

Preface by Sir Bernard Lovell
Director of the Nuffield Radio
Astronomy Laboratories
Jodrell Bank, England

Macmillan & Co Ltd London
St. Martin's Press New York
1964

MACMILLAN AND COMPANY LIMITED
ST. MARTIN'S STREET LONDON W.C.2
ALSO BOMBAY CALCUTTA MADRAS MELBOURNE

THE MACMILLAN COMPANY OF CANADA LIMITED
TORONTO

ST. MARTIN'S PRESS INC
NEW YORK

PRINTED IN BELGIUM BY
L'ANCIENNE SOCIETE ANONYME DE ROTOGRAVURE D'ART, BRUSSELS

PREFACE

We live in an age when tremendous interest is centred on the Moon. The contemporary desire for knowledge about our near neighbour in space has arisen for two reasons. First, two nations are spending vast sums of money in an attempt to land working instruments and then human beings on the lunar surface. Secondly, there has been much recent theoretical work on the problem of the origin of the solar system and it is realised that the Moon must hold important information about the early processes of formation of the bodies of the solar system.

The motive behind the first of these activities is only partly scientific ; nationalistic and military reasons are involved, as well as the scientific, in order to justify the expenditure of large sums on such gigantic technological feats. Nevertheless the scientific dividends will be of great importance. Lunik III has already, in 1959, given man his first information of the nature of the side of the Moon that is hidden from Earth and the subsequent American and Russian close approaches have given early information about such matters as the limit to the value of the Moon's magnetic field. A great step forward will be made when working instruments are actually landed on the lunar surface in order to record seismic disturbances, meteoric impacts and particularly when some analysis can be made of the nature of the surface layers and rocks of the Moon.

In the meantime our interest in such matters is greatly stimulated by the presentation of a modern lunar atlas. An authoritative and wonderfully illustrated atlas such as this is the base from which our future knowledge of the Moon will grow. The great advantage of this atlas is that it does not consist merely of a collection of beautiful photographs of the lunar landscape. It is written and produced in the modern idiom ; although earthbound it takes cognizance of the fact that we live in an age when new techniques are emerging for lunar studies.

The Moon has no atmosphere or at least any atmosphere which it possesses is so attenuated that no positive measurements of its density have yet been made. This has important advantages for scientists. It is possible to get excellent photographs of the surface from Earth, and in this respect the Moon is unique amongst our neighbours in the solar system. The planet Venus, for example, is so densely covered with cloud that even the biggest telescopes fail to reveal any detail about its surface features or even any information about the speed of rotation of the planet. Further, the absence of any significant lunar atmosphere means that there is no « weather » of the type we experience on Earth. Thus the surface of the Moon is untouched by the forces of erosion of wind and rain, which over periods of millions of years have determined the present appearance of our Earth. We can, therefore, expect the lunar features to be primeval in the sense that they contain the untouched evidence of the four and a half thousand million years of its existence.

This figure of four and a half thousand million years is one of the few real facts which we know about the early history of the solar system. Evidence from many sources gives this as the time scale of formation of the Earth, Moon and planets. But we do not know how the system was formed. There have been many theories. For example in the early decades of this century it was widely believed that the planetary system condensed from materia torn out of the Sun by a close encounter with a passing star — a rare accident giving a high degree of uniqueness to our home in space.

New knowledge soon led to the abandonment of this theory and nowadays we think it is more likely that the planetary system was formed by the accretion of particles in a nebula of dust and gas which originally surrounded the Sun. Whether the Sun was born as a star with this nebula, or subsequently acquired it in its journey through space is a matter for conjecture. On the question of the accretion *theory itself there are many grounds for anticipating that future observations may help to establish its validity and there can be little doubt that the lunar investigations will be critical.*

For example, were the mountains and maria revealed in the photographs in this atlas, caused by the impact of huge meteorites in the early stages after the main formation of the Moon had occurred or are they the result of volcanic action ? The accretion theory implies that the Moon and planets were formed in the cold state. Will the analysis of the lunar rocks support this theory, or will they indicate an originally molten condition ? Most critical of all, how did the Moon itself originate ? Were the Earth and the Moon originally one body, and was the Moon torn from the Earth by solar tidal forces, or did the Moon evolve as a satellite of the Earth by the accretion processes ?

These are some of the exciting questions which modern scientific developments may enable us to answer in the near future. The present book will for many years provide an authoritative and excellent basic guide to these new advances.

SIR BERNARD LOVELL.

INTRODUCTION

Will the expression « to promise the Moon » soon lose all meaning ? Many fanatics of interplanetary voyages are probably convinced of this since for them the landing on our satellite is only a question of years, if not indeed months. More cautious individuals, taking fuller account of the large number of problems which still have to be resolved, are far from unreservedly sharing such optimism, but it is nonetheless true that the Moon stirs human curiosity more and more each day. Besides, what can be more natural than this infatuation, if we think of the amazing progress made in the last 15 years or so, as much in the realm of lunar astronomy as in that of astronautics ?

Employing methods of observation as new as they are ingenious, astronomers of our time define in an extraordinarily precise manner the nature of the lunar surface, its temperature and the fluctuations which affect it. Powerful telescopes reveal today lunar formations and undulations of ground, the dimensions of which scarcely exceed a few hundred yards. As for the specialists of space research, they have not only sent an object to the Moon and obtained pictures of its other side, but all indications show that they will succeed in placing a robot there just as they will succeed in taking considerably sharper photographs at a shorter distance and at any angle. To put it briefly, these results and hopes have enhanced in a remarkable manner the interest which men have shown in our satellite since the beginning of time, and it is not without reason that many of them are already making great efforts to understand its complex motion and to study its characteristics. The present work makes a particular appeal to these enthusiastic amateur astronomers. It is made up of three parts. The first is a reminder of the elementary notions of lunar astronomy; this consists of 16 chapters devoted to the motions of the Moon, its structure and various phenomena for which it is responsible. The second part is in the form of a photographic atlas comprising 22 plates, which, largely overlapping, cover the whole known surface of the Moon. To each plate are attached two explanatory photographs on a reduced scale, one providing a means of locating the region under discussion and the other showing the names of visible lunar formations which have been adopted by the International Astronomical Union. A short text comments on the most remarkable of these formations. The atlas is completed, as it ought to be, by the provisional map of the other side of the Moon.

A modern work on the Moon cannot be conceived without the minimum of information on the subject of the possible means of its conquest. This is the aim of the third part which comprises four elementary chapters concerned with the principles of astronautics, a knowledge of which is necessary in order to understand what a journey to the Moon entails.

Finally, in order to facilitate the search for lunar formations a general alphabetical index has been provided which indicates the plate or plates on which these objects appear and, where necessary, the plate on which a commentary is given. As the majority of formations appear on several plates, it is very necessary to resort to this index in order to find the page containing the appropriate commentary.

* * *

This atlas differs considerably from the terrestrial atlases to which we have become accustomed in that it represents the various configurations as we see them, not as they exist in reality. The distortions that occur because the visible lunar surface is not plane but spherical and because the photographs are all taken from the same place are obviously all the greater as the photographed region is closer to the lunar edge. It is only at some future time when astronauts are in a position to wander freely around the Moon and to take all the necessary close-up shots that it will be possible to publish atlases of the classical type. Whatever the circumstances, the taking of photographs is subject to well defined conditions, for the sharpness of the objects depends essentially on the incident lighting. This explains why in certain plates the image only occupies a rather narrow part of the total surface, the rest remaining completely blank.

We may also express astonishment that in certain cases the explanatory locating photograph and the corresponding plate have quite different proportions. This further distortion is entirely due to differences in libration between the two photographs. The phenomenon of libration is itself explained in the first part of the book.

It must be remembered that the locating photograph is a composite one (put together by Lick Observatory) and is simply the two quarters side by side. For reasons which are explained in the work, the full Moon does not in fact display the profusion of detail which appears in the quarters and which are obviously of great value for the identification of various regions. The use of this device is particularly called for here.

One final point. Astronomers only know the Moon as seen in their telescopes, that is to say, upside down when compared to the fashion in which the ordinary mortal sees it. The photographs they take are therefore presented with the north at the bottom and this rule has naturally been respected except in a few exceptional cases where it is essential to show the lunar image as it is seen by the naked eye.

* * *

All the photographs in the atlas are from the collection of the late French astronomer Bernard Lyot, taken at the Pic du Midi Observatory and added to by his colleagues. M. André Danjon, the Director of the Paris Observatory, had the great kindness to put them at our disposal. They represent a unique collection and in the main these photographs have never yet been published. To M. Audouin Dollfus, a one-time colleague of Lyot, who personally directed the important task of printing the positives, I express my profound gratitude. I am particularly indebted to him for sending me a large number of his interesting documents and giving me advice throughout the whole work.

I should equally like to thank M. Jean Verbaandert, an astronomer at the Royal Observatory of Belgium, who offered to read through my texts and whose advice was always so very valuable. I should also like to thank M. Jean Dommanget, an astronomer at the Royal Observatory of Belgium, who provided me with some very useful information on his latest work, and M. Joseph Ruland, an amateur Belgian astronomer, who took the remarkable photographs of the eclipse on the 15th February, 1961, and of the Moon lit up by earthshine. Finally, I am happy to express my gratitude to the Directors of the Mount Wilson and Palomar Observatories and that of Lick, who have been kind enough to authorize the reproduction of their magnificent photographic documents.

TABLE OF CONTENTS

TABLE OF FIGURES

TABLE OF PHOTOGRAPHS

Abbreviations used :

P. M. — Pic du Midi Observatory.
W. & P. — Mounts Wilson and Palomar Observatories.
Paris Obs. — Paris Observatory.
Belg. Obs. — Royal Belgian Observatory.
Lick Obs. — Lick Observatory.
U.S. Inf. Serv. — United States Information Service.

BIBLIOGRAPHY

ALTER, D. and CLEMINSHAW, C. — *Pictorial astronomy* — Thomas. Y. Crowell Cy, New York, 1956.

BALDWIN, R.B. — *The face of the moon* — University of Chicago Press — 1958.

COUDERC, P., PECKER, J.P., SCHATZMAN, E. — *L'astronomie au jour le jour* — Gauthier-Villars, Paris, 1954.

COUDERC, P. — *Les étapes de l'astronomie* — Presses Universitaires de France, Paris, 1948.

DOLLFUS, A. — *Nouvelles recherches sur la lune* — « L'astronomie » — pp. 375 et seq. — Paris, 1961.

DOLLFUS, A. — *Communication made in December, 1960, to the International Astronomical Union in Leningrad.*

DOLLFUS, A. — *Etude des planètes par la polarisation de la lumière* — Supplément des « Annales d'Astrophysique », Paris, 1955.

FLAMMARION, C. and DANJON, A. — *Astronomie populaire Camille Flammarion* — voir Livre II. — DOLLFUS, A. — *La Lune* — Librairie Flammarion, Paris, 1955.

KUIPER, G.P. — *Exploration of the moon* — « Vistas in Astronautics », Vol. II, pp. 273 et ss. — Pergamon Press, Oxford, 1959.

KUIPER, G.P. — *Photographic Lunar Atlas* — University of Chicago Press, 1960.

PERELMAN. — *L'astronomie récréative* — Editions en langues étrangères, Moscow, 1958.

RUDAUX, L. and de VAUCOULEURS, G. — *Astronomie* — Larousse, Paris, 1952.

« SCIENCE ET VIE ». — *L'homme dans l'espace* — trimestriel N° 1, Paris, 1960.

SINTON, W.M. — *Temperature measurements on the Moon* — Lowell Observatory Bulletin, 5, 1, 1960.

UREY, H.C. — *Origin and nature of the Moon* — « Endeavour », XIX — N° 74 — Imperial Chemical Industries, London, 1960.

USSR ACADEMY OF SCIENCES. — *The other face of the Moon.* — Pergamon Press, Oxford, 1960.

USSR ACADEMY OF SCIENCES. — *Atlas de la face arrière de la lune* — Moscow, 1960.

WEIMER, Th. — *Atlas des profils lunaires* — Observatoire de Paris.

WILKINS, H.P. and MOORE, P. — *The Moon* — Faber & Faber, London, 1961.

First Part

FUNDAMENTAL ASTRONOMY

Nature and motions of the Moon

I

THE SATELLITE
AND FUNDAMENTAL LAWS

Kepler and Galileo

In its continual journey round the Sun, the Earth carries along
its satellite the Moon, which like a faithful dog turns tirelessly
around it. From the depths of antiquity astronomers worked
unceasingly to discover why and how the planets moved in the
sky, but it was not until the first years of the seventeenth
century that the correct reply to their questions was found.
This was the claim to fame of the German astronomer Johannes
Kepler who stated the three laws which are always linked with
his name, applicable as much to planets turning around the
Sun as to satellites orbiting another planet.
Kepler's first law determines the nature of the orbit : contrary
to what had been thought previously this is not a circle but
an ellipse one of whose foci is occupied by the body around
which the revolution is taking place. The second law, known
as the Law of Equal Areas, states that the movement is not
uniform and that it becomes more rapid as the two bodies more
closer to each other. It is, in fact, the confirmation of a well-
known phenomenon which is easily verified by circling round
the hand a stone attached to the end of a string ; if the latter
now goes round the arm, the stone comes closer into its centre
of rotation and starts to turn more and more quickly. The
third law consists in a relation between the time of the
revolution and the distance which separates the two bodies
concerned; from this therefore can be determined one of the
elements if the other one is known (Fig. 1).
In order to appreciate Kepler's work and to understand the
contribution which he brought to astronomy we must remember
that this indefatigable and remarkable mathematician was born
in 1571, that is to say, almost a century after the celebrated
Polish astronomer Copernicus. His work, therefore, took place
at a time when, apart from Galileo who was seven years older
than he, no-one yet dared make a positive pronouncement on
the heliocentric system which was in direct opposition to the
then current philosophy. Besides, another quite significant thing
is that Copernicus issued only a short time before his death
the book in which he established that the Sun was at the centre
of the world and that the planets including the Earth turned
around it.
Kepler was a mystic : convinced that the world was governed
by certain harmonies, he used this term a great deal in the
work which he published in 1618. He was a fervent supporter
of the theory of Copernicus but this did not prevent him from
expressing a lively admiration for Tycho Brahe, the celebrated
Danish astronomer, who was its adversary. He had the
inestimable luck of inheriting the notes in which Brahe had
written down his innumerable observations, and being a
mathematician of the first order he studied all the results

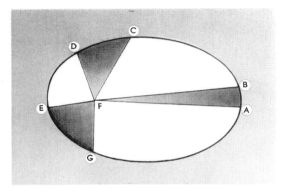

*Fig. 1. — Kepler's Laws. Kepler's laws are applicable
to all celestial bodies in motion. As far as the planets
revolving round the Sun are concerned, these laws
can be stated as follows :*

*1st law. The planetary orbits are ellipses with the
Sun at one focus.*

*2nd law. The radius vector sweeps out equal areas
in equal times.*

*3rd law. The squares of the periodic times of any
revolution are proportional to the cubes of the
mean distances of the planets from the Sun.*
The figure illustrates the second law, generally
known as the « law of areas ». The planet traverses
the unequal portions of the ellipse AB, CD and
EG in equal times, since the areas FAB, FCD
and FEG are equal.

The third law allows one to calculate either the
distance of the planet from the Sun if the revolution
period is known, or this period if the distance is
known. It can be written

$$\frac{T^2_1}{T^2_2} = \frac{D^3_1}{D^3_2}$$

If we take as unity, on the one hand the mean
Earth-Sun distance (the Astronomical Unit), and on
the other the year, the formula can be simplified
to become :

$$\frac{T^2}{1^2} = \frac{D^3}{1^3} \qquad or \qquad T^2 = D^3$$

Examples. 1) Find the revolutionary period of
Jupiter, given that this planet is at a distance of
5.2 astronomical units from the Sun. Then from
the formula, $\quad T = \sqrt{5.2^3} = 11.8\ years.$
2) What is the distance of Saturn from the Sun,
given its period of revolution as 29.4 earth years ?
This distance is given by the formula $D = \sqrt[3]{T^2}$
therefore in this case

$$D = \sqrt[3]{29.4^2} = 9.5\ a.\ u.$$

or about 1400 million kilometres.

with infinite patience in order to extract his laws from them. There, however, his efforts ceased, for he did not go so far as to try and discover the very causes of the motions which he had succeeded in defining so perfectly. Seen from this angle, his work presents therefore an essentially empirical character.

At the same time, Galileo established for his part the laws which govern falling bodies but he also went no further than stating the facts without finding out the reasons. This inspired physicist postulated moreover one of the most important principles of mechanics, that of inertia, according to which every body tends to keep indefinitely its state of rest or of motion, but he did not see any connection between the mechanics of Kepler which he believed was only applicable to celestial bodies and the mechanics that he was in the process of founding, which according to him was only concerned with terrestrial objects.

Newton

It was only in fact at the end of the seventeenth century that a new man of genius, no doubt the greatest of them all, demonstrated that the laws of Kepler and of Galileo were derived from one and the same principle : gravitation or universal attraction. This man was Isaac Newton who was born in 1643, at almost the exact moment when Galileo died.

In his work which is universally considered one of the purest masterpieces of thought, *Mathematical Principles of Natural Philosophy*, Newton proves the identity which exists between the forces which one heavenly body exerts on another and the gravity which obtains on the surface of the Earth. His law is of astonishing simplicity but it is sufficient to explain all the celestial phenomena whilst proving irrefutably that there is only one system of mechanics. This law states that the attraction existing between two particles of matter is directly proportional to the product of their masses and inversely proportional to the square of the distance which separates their centres of gravity.

Legend has it that the fundamental law of universal gravitation came to life in Newton's mind when in the moonlight he had noticed the fall of an apple. « Why », he is said to have asked himself, « does this apple fall on to the Earth and not the Moon ? » He would have already guessed that the Moon was in fact falling but that obeying the law of inertia it tended at the same time to move further away, following a straight line perpendicular to the direction of its fall. These two forces, gravity and inertia, acting simultaneously would therefore reach an equilibrium at each instant and bring about the revolution of the Moon around the Earth.

This is in fact the origin of this motion which a very simple but purely theoretical example can demonstrate without it being necessary to have recourse to any mathematical formula. A gun pointing horizontally in a very elevated position fires a shell. Elementary ballistics teaches us that the trajectory followed by the projectile depends essentially on two factors. The power of the gun or more exactly the active force given to the shell, and the force of gravity, the value of which is determined by the height of the situation of the gun (Fig. 2). In fact there is a third factor, the resistance of the air, but this element can be ignored here as it has no effect in the spaces where satellites are moving. If there were no gravity the shell would leave

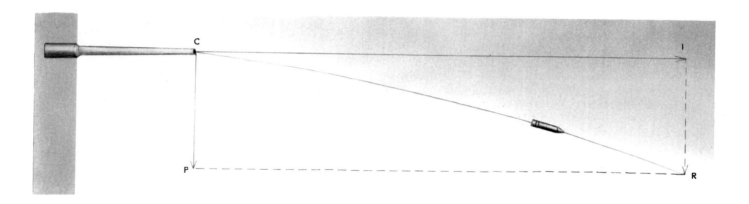

Fig. 2. — Forces acting on a projectile. *If the gun were to fire the shell with no gravity present, the projectile, impelled by its inertia, would take up the horizontal trajectory C I. On the other hand, if the shell was just dropped from the barrel, it would be acted on by the force of gravity alone and would fall, following the line of the perpendicular C P. As the two forces act at the same time, the true trajectory is C R.*

the gun in a straight line and would move away indefinitely according to the principle of inertia ; in this case there would be simply only a transference of position. On the contrary, if gravity were the sole force, that is to say, instead of being fired the projectile was simply pushed out of the gun, it would instantaneously make its way towards the centre of the Earth — there would simply be a fall. As the two actions act in fact simultaneously the shell goes forward the same distance as if the firing force had acted alone, whilst at the same time falling the same distance as if merely gravity had exercised its attraction. The trajectory is consequently a curve which meets the Earth's surface at a distance dependent upon the power of the gun, that is to say according to the initial speed communicated to the projectile.

However, if the point of impact is to be calculated in a more precise manner we must then take account of an element which has only a very slight importance when we are dealing with short range shots but which becomes of great importance when the range becomes very long, namely, the curvature of the Earth. It is easy to demonstrate that the curvature of the Earth exercises a favourable influence on the distance reached by the projectile since the surface seems to slip away from it ; contact is made, therefore, further away than if the terrestrial surface was perfectly flat. The two curves representing respectively the trajectory of the shell and the profile of the Earth present therefore a certain parallelism, and this is accentuated as the power of the gun increases (Fig. 3). Finally, it can be logically stated that if we can sufficiently increase the initial

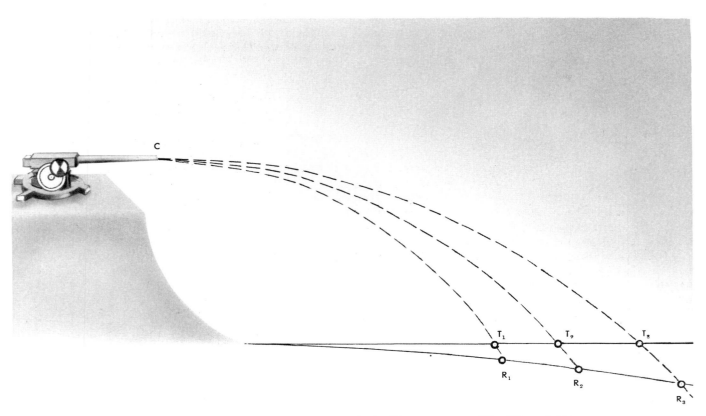

Fig. 3. — Influence of the curvature of the Earth. *The trajectories CT_1, CT_2 and CT_3 are more and more extended. Due to the curvature of the Earth, the points of impact R_1, R_2 and R_3 are proportionally considerably further away than the points T_1, T_2 and T_3. If the energy transferred to the shell is sufficient, the trajectory becomes ultimately parallel to the ground.*

velocity the projectile will ultimately run parallel to the Earth's surface and will never touch it ; it becomes an artificial satellite and begins to turn indefinitely around the Earth such as, for example, the Moon.

There is, however, an enormous difference between the time taken by the revolution of the Moon and that of an artificial satellite. The first takes 28 days to complete its revolution which corresponds to a transversal displacement of 1 kilometre per second approximately (1.017 exactly). As for the second, it takes roughly an hour and a half to make a complete orbit at a height of some thousand kilometres and this represents a velocity of about 8000 metres per second. Now it is precisely this question which was the object of Newton's researches and which allowed him to find his law. By identifying the attraction exercised by the Earth on the Moon with gravity the celebrated physicist calculated the value which this gravity must have at the lunar distance, it being admitted that it would weaken proportionally as the square of the separation. Further, he calculated the number of metres by which the Moon would normally fall towards the Earth during the course of a second and it was thus that he was able to verify the perfect accuracy of his intuition : the distance of this « fall » was exactly equal to the number of metres that the Moon would have moved away from the Earth during the same second if, set free from terrestrial attraction, it had been able to escape at a tangent (Fig. 4).

In announcing the law of universal gravitation, Newton had gone considerably further than Kepler and Galileo into research of the fundamental causes governing the motion of stars. He defined the forces which caused these motions and further he laid the foundations of infinitesimal calculus, called by him the method of fluxions, which allowed him to prove that by applying his laws to celestial bodies one came to the same conclusion as Kepler whose law establishes the shape of planetary orbits. In modern mathematical language one would merely state that the law of universal gravitation provides the elements of a differential equation concerning the motion of bodies in space ; by a process of integration we can reach a formula which indicates that the trajectory is an ellipse. Besides, the fame of the English physicist is even more considerable since universal gravitation does not only explain the type of movement which animates the bodies in the universe, it also gives the quantitative reason of other astronomical phenomena which until that time had been stated but not demonstrated. Amongst these we must mention : perturbations caused by the movements of planets, the precession of the equinoxes, tides, and even the flattening of the Earth at the poles.

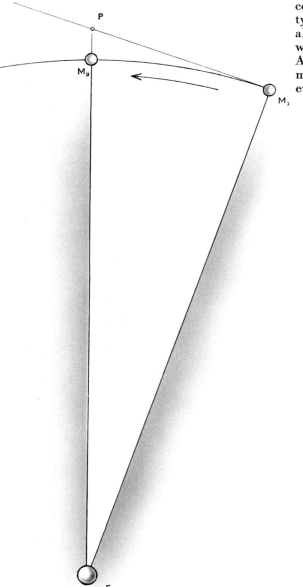

Fig. 4. The Moon and Newton's Law. *If M_1 and M_2 represent the successive positions of the Moon separated by a second of time, $P M_2$ represents the distance through which the Moon has effectively « fallen » towards the Earth, since it would have followed the path M_1P if the Earth had not attracted it. The length of the portion $P M_2$ can be calculated without difficulty, given the period of the Moon's revolution and its distance from the Earth. It is equal to 1.35 millimetres.*
In accordance with the law concerning falling bodies postulated by Galileo, any mass falling in space towards the Earth's surface covers a distance of 4.9 metres during the first second. This path represents 3,600 times the distance the Moon falls in the same time; now 3,600 is precisely the square of 60 and the Moon is 60 times further from the centre of the Earth than is the Earth's surface. The accuracy of Newton's law could not be better demonstrated.

II

THE REVOLUTION
OF THE MOON
AROUND THE EARTH

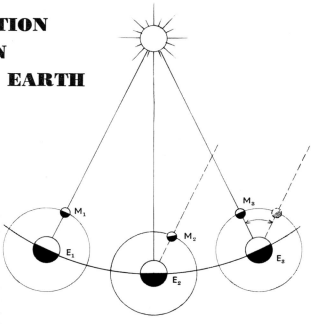

Sidereal and Synodic Revolutions

For many reasons the Moon is the subject of a considerable number of motions which in combination make it trace out in space an extremely complex trajectory. Its fundamental motion is that which causes it to go round the Earth : a complete orbit, that is to say a sidereal revolution, requires 27 days 7 hours 43 minutes and 11 seconds. At the end of this period the Earth-Moon axis is exactly in the same position in relation to the stars as it was at the beginning. So much cannot be said, however, concerning its orientation with respect to the Sun, for the Earth itself goes around the Sun whilst the Moon is orbiting the Earth. As a consequence of this other motion it is necessary for our satellite to continue its course for a further two days in order that the three bodies can return to their relative initial positions : to this longer revolution has been given the name of lunation or synodic revolution, the first of these terms recalling the known succession of the phases of the Moon. The duration of a lunation is 29 days 12 hours 44 minutes and 2 seconds (Fig. 5).

Fig. 5. Sidereal revolution and synodic revolution. *During the time taken for the Earth to pass from E_1 to E_2, the Moon completes a full circle (360°), that is a sidereal revolution. The axis EM thus finds itself in the same position with respect to the stars but not with respect to the Sun. In order for the three bodies to be once again in the same straight line, the Moon must continue its path until the Earth reaches the point E_3. The time taken by the Moon in going from M_1 to M_3 is known as the synodic revolution or lunation. (For the sake of clarity the drawing is not to scale; the distance E_1 to E_2 is obviously much greater than E_2 to E_3.)*

Real and Apparent Motion

In order to understand the motion of the Moon it is necessary at the beginning to recall those to which our own sphere is subject. The Earth describes in 365 days 6 hours a complete revolution around the Sun. It also turns on its own axis in 24 hours but its axis of rotation is not perpendicular to the plane of its orbit, that is to say to the plane of the *ecliptic* : it is inclined to the ecliptic at an angle of 66° 33' which is the same thing as saying that the planes of the equator and the ecliptic make between them an angle of 23° 27' (Fig. 6). From our terrestrial observatory we can determine the real motion of our sphere only by the apparent motion it gives to all the other heavenly bodies. On the one hand the rotation of the Earth on its own axis creates the illusion that it is the Sun and at the same time the whole celestial vault which turns around us. On the other hand the annual revolution leads us to think that the Sun makes its progress through the stars and traverses in a year the twelve constellations of the Zodiac (Fig. 7). Finally, the inclination of the axis of rotation also plays its part in the complete illusion : it is the origin of the variations which the apparent trajectory of the Sun suffers daily and of the differences in duration during which the Sun remains above the horizon.

Like the Sun, the Moon seems each day to trace a curve from East to West in the sky but somewhat more slowly. As the direction of its proper motion is in effect opposed to that of

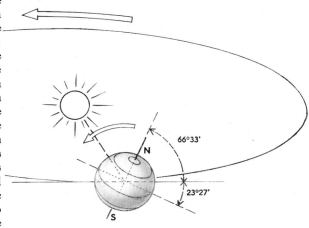

Fig. 6. — Inclination of the Earth's axis to the plane of the ecliptic. *The plane which contains the Earth's orbit (and naturally the Sun) is the plane of the ecliptic. The Earth's axis of rotation NS is inclined to this plane at an angle of 66° 33'. Consequently, the plane of the terrestrial equator is likewise inclined to that of the ecliptic at an angle of 23° 27'.*

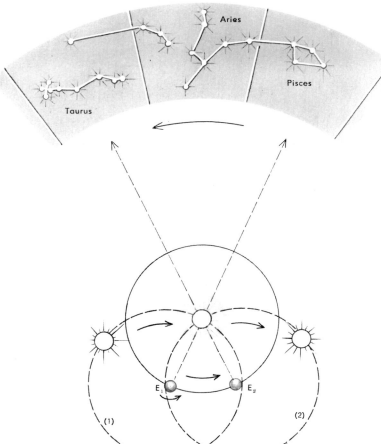

Fig. 7. — Apparent orbits of the Sun. E_1 *indicates the position of the Earth in March; an observer capable of perceiving the stars behind the Sun would see the latter shining in the constellation of Pisces. But as the Earth pivots on its axis, the observer has the impression that the whole celestial vault is turning above his head; in particular the Sun describes the apparent orbit 1. As, furthermore, the Earth continues its annual revolution around the Sun, it is in the position E_2 two months later; the observer, who in May once again looked at the Sun's position amongst the stars, would discover that it was now in the constellation of Taurus. Its apparent orbit would then be curve 2.*

the apparent motion of the sky, our satellite trails in relation to the other heavenly bodies. Thus we see it every day rising and setting a little later, the daily average of this delay being 50 minutes 30 seconds.

To tell the truth, we can only conveniently appreciate the proper motion of the Moon if the Earth ceased to turn on its axis. If such a state of affairs could be realized the idea of day would disappear *ipso facto* but in supposing that our sphere would nevertheless continue its revolution around the Sun the year would continue to exist ; to put it another way, the second apparent motion of the Sun would remain and we would again see it turning around us with the difference that a complete orbit would last a whole year. The Sun would take, therefore, six months to cross the heavenly vault after which we would be plunged into darkness for a period of the same duration. As for the Moon, we would see it likewise slowly moving, although it would be $12\frac{1}{4}$ times faster than the Sun. During the six months of darkness we would be able to observe it six times as it crossed the sky but these half lunations which we would successively witness would undergo a certain displacement at each passage. At the beginning of the nocturnal period the Moon would rise as a full Moon and would set in its new phase ; in the middle of the period, the half lunation would extend from the first to the last quarter and at the end of the period it would go from the new phase to the full Moon.

Let us suppose finally that our sphere itself ceases to turn around the Sun ; then one of its halves would be constantly bathed in sunlight whilst the other would remain in eternal night. From the dark hemisphere we would then see the Moon periodically describe its half orbit as in the preceding hypothesis but without any phase displacement at each passage. It would no longer be possible then to speak of synodic revolution since this would have become identical with the sidereal revolution.

These considerations, of course, only concern a completely imaginary world but nevertheless they serve to demonstrate to what extent the motions of our sphere confuse in our eyes those which in reality move the heavenly bodies. They also show why it took humanity such a long time to establish the true basis of the solar system.

The Double Planet

Although from many points of view the Earth and the Moon scarcely resemble each other they nevertheless constitute a unique ensemble in the solar system. In fact, if their respective volumes as well as their masses differ appreciably these differences are indeed very small compared with those which can be seen in other systems of the same kind. The following systems which from this point of view are classified immediately after that of the Earth and Moon are particularly eloquent. The diameter of Neptune is ten times greater than that of its satellite Triton whilst the diameter of the Earth is scarcely four times that of the Moon. The mass of Jupiter is 10,000 times greater than that of its third satellite whilst the mass of the Earth is equal to 81.5 times that of the Moon. Besides, the distance which separates the Earth from the Moon is itself remarkable — it is classed amongst the smallest (when considered in proportion, of course).

For these various reasons the Earth-Moon system is sometimes called a *double planet* by analogy with the title *double star* which is given to numerous stellar groups. These stars, whose dimensions are comparable one with another, move in the sky, each one describing an elliptical orbit around their common centre of gravity. However, the Earth-Moon set-up is rather different, for the common centre of gravity is situated within our sphere ; actually it is about three-quarters of the radius from the centre. In any case when we consider precisely the relative movements of the Earth and the Moon in space we must take account of the following facts : whilst the Moon describes its Keplerian ellipse around the centre of gravity common to our sphere and its satellite, the centre of the Earth itself goes round this same point (Fig. 8). Besides, the point which in a year describes the elliptical orbit around the Sun is not the centre of the Earth but the common centre of gravity (Fig. 9).

When we are considering this latter idea, another point must be made clear : the shape in space of the trajectory followed by the Moon. The comparison which has been made between the Earth-Moon system and the dog turning around its master as they go for a walk would seem to suggest that this trajectory is a curve similar to a series of loops. This, however, is not true, for the speed with which the Earth is carried along around the

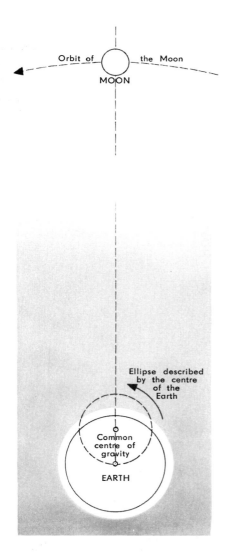

Fig. 8. — The rotation of the Earth and the Moon around their common centre of gravity. *The common centre of gravity of the Earth and the Moon is determined by the respective mass of the two bodies. If they were equal, the centre of gravity would be exactly halfway between the two spheres. But as the mass of the Earth is 81.5 times that of the Moon, it is situated 81.5 times nearer the centre of the Earth. In fact, it is inside the latter, about 4,650 kilometres from the centre, so that during the time taken for a revolution of the Moon the centre of the Earth itself describes a closed circle of radius less than 5,000 kilometres.*

Fig. 9. — The ellipse described around the Sun by the common centre of gravity of the Earth-Moon system. *The centres of the Earth and the Moon both turn around their common centre of gravity. It is this latter point which in fact describes the ellipse around the Sun.*

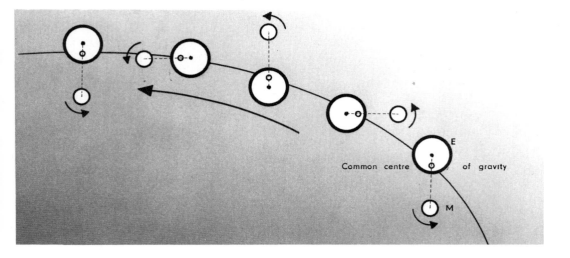

Sun is much greater (30 times greater) than the speed of the revolution of the Moon around the Earth. The result therefore is that the lunar trajectory is seen in the form of a sinuous line passing alternately from one side to the other of the Earth (Fig. 10). Finally, the distance of the Earth to the Sun being 400 times greater than that which separates our sphere from the Moon, the trajectory of the latter in space differs proportionally very little from that of the Earth ; in fact, it is so slight that despite its sinuosity it remains at each point concave on the side facing the Sun (Fig. 11).

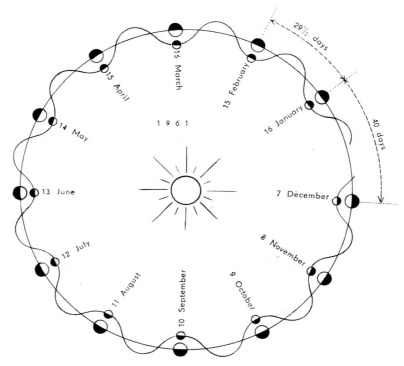

Fig. 10. — Diagram of the lunar path in space. *Contrary to what one might believe, the path of the Moon in space is not made up of a series of loops around the Earth. It is a wavy line passing in turn from one side of our sphere to the other. Note the displacement which occurs in the lunation from one year to the next : as the synodic revolution is 29 ½ days, 12 lunations take a little over 354 days, about 11 days less than a year.*

Fig. 11. — True aspect of lunar and terrestrial paths. *Just like the Earth's path, that of the Moon is constantly concave towards the Sun.*

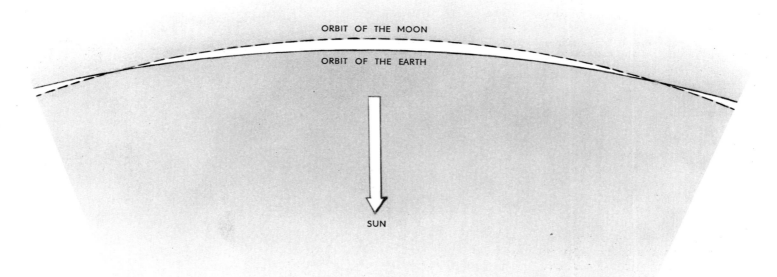

III

THE PHASES
OF THE MOON

The Lunar Albedo

Our satellite is an opaque body which does not give out any light of its own ; if it shines in space this is because it reflects a fraction of the light sent to it by the Sun, but its *albedo*, that is to say, its power of reflection, is extremely weak. It is the nature of the materials which constitute the surface of a planet which determines its albedo ; that of the Earth is 0.40 whilst that of the Moon is only 0.07 which means that our satellite absorbs 93 per cent of the light which it receives from the Sun. Since the Moon describes in the sky a trajectory analogous to that of the Sun but, of course, more slowly, its shining portion, that is to say the only part which we are able to see, changes constantly, depending upon the Moon's position with respect to the Earth and the Sun. The varying aspects that the Moon assumes as a consequence of the angle under which it is illuminated are denoted *phases*.

The Waxing Moon

The plane in which the Moon moves is very close to that of the ecliptic. In order to explain the phenomenon of its phases in a simple way we can without committing any appreciable error suppose these planes to be the same (Fig. 12). When our satellite is in the same direction as the Sun it turns its non-illuminated face towards us and we cannot see anything of it. This is the moment of the *new Moon* or, as astronomers call it, *conjunction*. In fact, if the planes of the terrestrial and lunar orbits were indeed the same, the Moon would pass exactly in front of the Sun at each conjunction and would consequently eclipse it ; the few degrees with which these two heavenly bodies are generally separated from each other at this time are responsible for the rarity of eclipses. Two days after the new Moon and sometimes even the following day, the angle made by the direction of the Moon and the Sun is sufficiently great for a very feeble part of the lunar disc to be visible to our eyes : we see then a very thin cres-

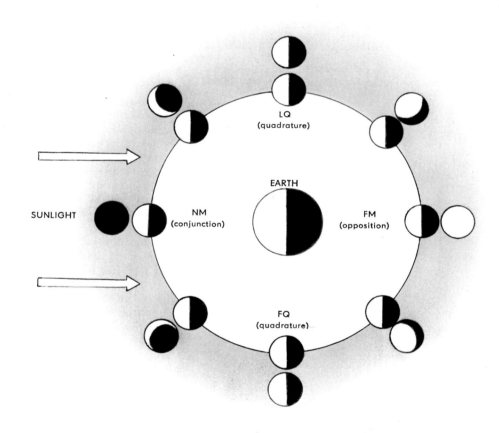

Fig. 12. — The phases of the Moon. *The series of discs drawn around the outside of the circle represent the Moon as seen from the Earth at different phases of the lunation. The discs on the circle show the same Moon as seen by an observer in space in a direction perpendicular to the plane of the Moon's orbit.*

25

cent, the convex side of which is turned towards the Sun. The appearance of this delicate shape has always been invested with such an importance — certain religions have even chosen this time to fix the beginning of a ritual period — that many people call it incorrectly the new Moon. Others imagine that the moment in which the first lunar crescent can be seen depends on the *age of the Moon*, that is to say, on the number of hours which have gone by since conjunction. This is equally inexact since for many reasons which will be examined further on, the slight separation between the positions of the Sun and the Moon at the moment when the latter is new varies at each synodic revolution. Moreover, the apparent speed of our satellite changes so that finally the angle made between the directions of the two bodies — an angle which alone is accountable for the visibility of the crescent — is in no way connected with the age of the Moon in any fixed manner. It has been established that only under exceptional circumstances can this angle be less than 10°.

Earthshine. — *Photo 1.* — *On the part illuminated by earthshine the marks and outlines which appear at the time of the full Moon can be easily seen.*
(*Photo Joseph Ruland.*)

Fig. 13. — *The shape of the crescent Moon. The limb, since it is the edge of the lunar sphere, can clearly be seen to be part of a circle but the terminator, which is a half circle drawn on a sphere, appears in perspective to be part of an ellipse.*

Although about the time of the new Moon, all the light that our satellite receives directly from the Sun falls on the hemisphere opposed to that which faces us, it would be false to say that the latter is the object of no illumination ; on the contrary, it even receives quite an appreciable illumination and in order to convince ourselves of this, all we have to do is to transport ourselves in our mind to this region. Naturally it would be the middle of the night there but we could see the Earth shining in the sky just as on Earth we can see the full Moon. This « earthlight », which astronauts long to contemplate, is very much more luminous than moonlight for two reasons : the greater surface of the terrestrial disc (13.5 times greater than the lunar disc) and the greater value of terrestrial albedo (6 times greater). It has been calculated that the « full Earth » sends to our satellite 40 to 50 times more light than the full Moon sends in our direction.

We cannot perceive anything of this reflected light from our terrestrial observatory on the day of the new Moon because of the dazzle created by solar radiation, but this is not so a little before or after this date. Thus if, for example, two days after conjunction we observe the Moon immediately after sunset before night has completely fallen, we can clearly distinguish at the side of the thin luminous crescent the rest of the disc feebly illuminated. Certain people whose visual acuity is particularly great can even perceive minute details. The name *earthshine* has been given to this indirect illumination which constitutes one of the most curious phenomena which our satellite offers us and which has intrigued scientists for many centuries. This is perhaps rather surprising when we consider the accurate explanations given by men of science of ancient times about even more complicated celestial phenomena. Leonardo da Vinci and Kepler are normally considered to be the first to have correctly shown the origin of earthshine.

As the angle defined by the direction of the Sun and the Moon increases the lunar crescent becomes broader. The shape it depicts in the sky is limited on one side by the outer edge of the disc which is called the *limb*, and on the other by the line which separates the illuminated region from that which is in the shadow. This line has received the name of terminator, or to be more exact the *morning terminator*, since an observer on the Moon would see the Sun rise at each one of these points. Contrary to the way in which numerous artists have represented the terminator the curve does not have the form of a circular arc but rather that of an elliptical arc according to the laws of geometry and perspective (Fig. 13).

When the Moon becomes about a week old its visible part takes the shape of a semicircle : this is the *first quarter or quadrature*. The terminator is then a straight line and divides the lunar disc into two equal parts. At this time the lag of the Moon on the Sun is such that from afternoon on we can see it in the sky. At the time of the first quarter earthshine is practically non-existent. It decreases in fact from day to day

The Phases of the Moon

(Photos Mount Wilson and Palomar Observatories — 100-inch telescope.)

The Moon three days old. Photo 2.

The Moon five days old. Photo 3.

The Moon 20 days old. Photo 7.

Full Moon. — Photo 6.

following its appearance, not only because it is more and more covered up by the luminous crescent which is growing but also because, as the phases of the Earth are inverse to the phases of the Moon, the intensity of earthlight is itself diminishing.

After the first quarter the visible part of the Moon covers progressively more than half the disc ; the terminator again assumes an elliptical shape but its concavity is in the opposite direction. At the end of another week the entire disc is directly illuminated. The Moon has reached the limit of its waxing ; it rises at the exact moment that the Sun sets : this is the period of *full Moon* or *opposition*.

The Waning Moon

The waning of the Moon commences immediately : a new line of demarcation between light and shade grows on the side of the same limb as at the beginning of lunation but it marks out in the opposite sense the dark and light zones. This is the *evening terminator*, the name of which is self-explanatory and which progresses in the same way across the lunar disc ; as a consequence the illuminated part gradually retreats. This third phase is in fact the opposite of the preceding, the Moon now rising after sunset.

As for the fourth phase, it begins when the evening terminator cuts the lunar disc in two equal parts by a straight line and brings about in this manner the *last quarter*, opposite to the first. The illuminated part then progressively assumes the shape of an increasingly narrow crescent the direction of which is opposite to that of the first crescent. The Moon now rises after midnight and the earthshine reappears ; it becomes more and more visible each day. Finally, the time lag of the Moon reaches 24 hours ; lunation is complete and the two bodies, Sun and Moon, are once more in conjunction.

The Orientation of the Lunar Crescent

The orientation of the Moon in space is often the cause of some puzzlement. Although we generally know the mnemonics which allow us to establish if we are looking at the first or the last quarter, we are sometimes intrigued by the way in which the Moon seems to seesaw in the sky from one day to the next. Logically speaking the straight line joining the two *cusps*, that is to say the extremities of the crescent, should be perpendicular at the middle to the straight line which joins this point to the Sun. Now if this can be verified when the crescent is very thin, it is no longer true when the Moon is in its first quarter or has gone beyond this stage. Nothing can show the progressive orientation of the lunar crescent better than a photographic montage obtained by a daily photograph on the same plate taken with a rigidly fixed camera. If we suppose the latter pointed towards that portion of the heavens occupied by the Moon during the first half of a lunation, our satellite would appear on the final photograph numerous times in successive positions and aspects. Joining together the centre of all these lunar images we would obtain a curve cutting perpendicularly each one of the straight lines joining the two cusps, a curve which would continue as far as the Sun. This would tend to make us believe that a ray of sunlight is curved. It obviously is not so and it is simply a question of an optical illusion : the Sun's rays are incontestably rectilinear, but the line which appears to our eyes is simply the projection of this ray on the spherical vault of the sky which itself is curved (Fig. 14).

Fig. 14. — Orientation of the Moon in the sky. An imaginary ray of sunlight joining the centres of the Moon depicted in various parts of the sky, according to the different phases, is in fact a straight line. Nevertheless it appears curved to us because we can only see it projected on to the curving background of the sky.

← *The Phases of the Moon*

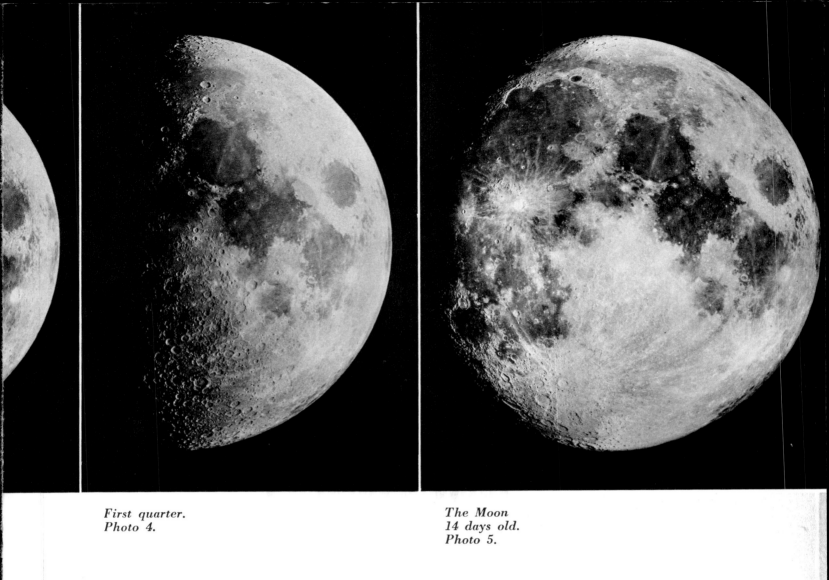

First quarter.
Photo 4.

The Moon
14 days old.
Photo 5.

Last quarter.
Photo 8.

The Moon
23 days old.
Photo 9.

The Moon
26 days old.
Photo 10.

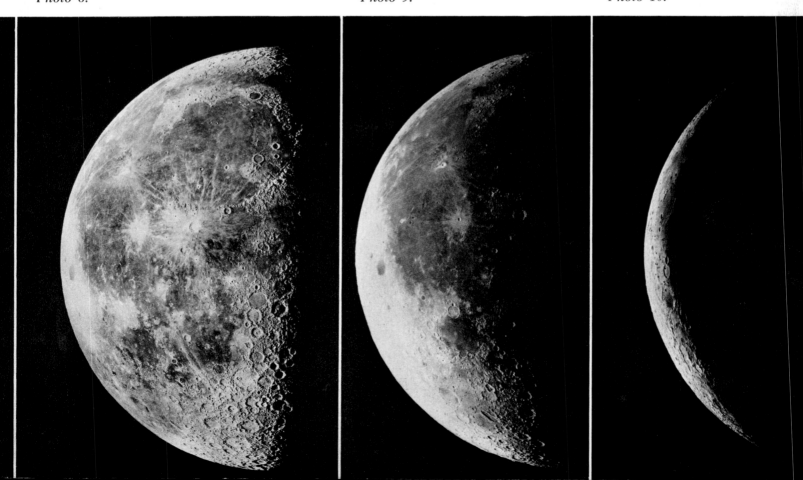

IV

DISTANCE, SURFACE AREA
AND MASS OF THE MOON

Maximum and Minimum Distances

The mean distance which separates the centre of the Earth from the centre of the Moon is 384,000 kilometres which is 60 times the Earth's radius ; 30 terrestrial spheres would be needed, therefore, to cover this distance if we were able to get them in a straight line. This relatively small figure always surprises the uninitiated and it also provides, as we have said before, one of the reasons which justify the name « double planet » given to the Earth-Moon system.

The orbit of the Moon is elliptical like that of all the heavenly bodies but its eccentricity is more pronounced than that of the Earth's orbit ; 1/18 or 0.055 as against 0.017. The point on the lunar orbit which is furthest

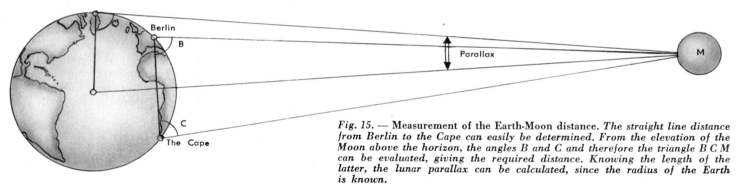

Fig. 15. — Measurement of the Earth-Moon distance. *The straight line distance from Berlin to the Cape can easily be determined. From the elevation of the Moon above the horizon, the angles B and C and therefore the triangle B C M can be evaluated, giving the required distance. Knowing the length of the latter, the lunar parallax can be calculated, since the radius of the Earth is known.*

from the Earth, known as *apogee*, has a mean distance of 405,000 kilometres (the maximum distance being 406,800 kilometres) ; for the nearest point or *perigee* the mean is 363,000 kilometres from the Earth (the minimum distance being 356.500 kilometres). The Earth-Moon distance varies therefore between 28 and 32 terrestrial diameters which is quite appreciable. The terrestrial surface is separated from the lunar surface at the moment of closest approach by 348,000 kilometres.

Various methods have been considered in order to calculate the Earth-Moon distance but the usual one is simply that used by surveyors to measure the distance of an object which they cannot reach. The preliminary operation is the establishment of a baseline, the length of which must be very exactly known and which must be traced as much as possible in a direction perpendicular to that of the object under consideration. By pointing a telescope towards the latter from each of the two extremities of the baseline in turn, a triangle can be worked out from which it is easy to calculate each part and consequently the desired distance. The accuracy of this measurement depends on the length of the baseline chosen. Given, however, that we should seek a solution in which the lines of sight cut each other at right angles, the ideal situation consists in arranging for a baseline with a length equivalent to the estimated distance of the desired object. Of course, when it is a question of measuring an enormous distance such as that of the Earth to the Moon, this last requirement is illusory and we must be content with the longest possible baseline. In this case, however, in order to take account of the condition of perpendicularity between the direction of the Moon and that of the baseline, we adopt, for the latter, part of a meridian. The problem is complicated somewhat by the fact that this baseline is not situated in one plane.

This procedure was first adopted in 1751 by the French astronomers Lalande and La Caille. To accomplish this time-honoured exploit they went respectively to Berlin and to the Cape which are both to all intents and purposes situated on the same meridian. The results which they obtained were extraordinarily precise and are still today a cause for astonishment when we consider the rudimentary means which they had at their disposal (Fig. 15).

Other methods have been used since then amongst which the most spectacular is that which calls on the properties of radar. The principle of this system of detection is remarkably simple : it is that of an echo. A shout uttered some distance from a wall is reflected from this and as it returns to its point of transmission allows us to calculate the distance of the obstacle since we know the velocity of the propagation of sound. The effect is the same with a radio signal sent into space : it is reflected on meeting a conducting body during its journey and reception of the ensuing echo at the point of emission allows us to calculate the distance to the obstacle. However, whereas sound is propagated at a speed of 340 metres per second, radio waves travel through space at 300,000 kilometres per second — in other words roughly a million times more rapidly. This necessitates apparatus capable of measuring minute intervals of time, a millionth of a second at least. On the 22nd January 1946 at 11 p.m. the first measurement of this distance was made and this corresponded exactly to the distance which had been determined beforehand (2½ seconds approximately).

By measuring the distance of the Moon we establish *ipso facto* its *parallax*, that is to say the angle made by the radius of the Earth as seen by an observer placed at the centre of the Moon. The mean value of this parallax is 57', almost one degree. The mean angle made by the Moon's radius as seen from the Earth is 15' 32". The apparent mean diameter of our satellite is then very nearly half a degree ; in fact it varies between 29' 21" and 33' 30". It is a curious fact however that this gives errors in estimation as great as they are frequent. Many people, when asked for the dimensions which a round object held at arm's length would have to possess in order to mask the Moon, give figures from 10 tot 40 times too great. It is true that the correct reply is rather unexpected : a disc half a centimetre in diameter, scarcely the cross-section of a cigarette.

Another illusion currently believed is that the Moon has a greater apparent diameter when it is on the horizon than when it is high in the sky. Not only is there nothing in this, but it is the opposite which is true since between these two distances there is the difference of an Earth radius which represents nevertheless a sixtieth of the total value (Fig. 16). A large number of scientists have tried to explain this paradox. Some have argued that the Moon appears greater on the horizon because we see it alongside other objects with which we can compare it, which is not so when it is high in the sky. This is a debatable point, for the illusion is the same when the Moon is on the horizon above the sea where no point of comparison exists. Others have advanced the hypothesis that an object appears greater when it can be seen directly in front of us than when we have to lean over backwards to see it, but to tell the truth no explanation has yet been universally admitted to justify this singular illusion.

As the distance of the Moon is known as well as its apparent diameter, its real diameter can be easily calculated ; it is 3476 kilometres, that is to say 0.272 times that of the Earth. Four Moons placed in a row would make a line somewhat longer than the diameter of the Earth (Fig. 17).

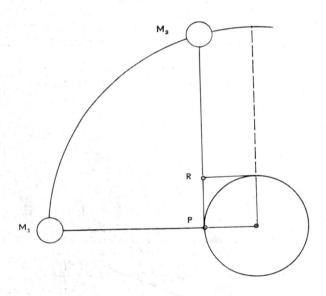

Fig. 16. — Moon-zenith and Moon-horizon distances compared. *When the Moon is at M_1, it is at the zenith for an observer at P. Its distance is therefore $P M_1$. When it is at M_2 it is on the horizon and the distance is $P M_2$. Now $P M_1 = R M_2$ therefore $P M_2 = P M_1 + P R$ namely $P M_1 +$ one Earth radius.*

Surface Area and Mass

The surface area of our satellite is 13.46 times less than that of our sphere ; the respective values are 37,800,000 km² and 510,000,000 km². As for the volume of the Moon it is more than 50 times less than that of the Earth. The mass of the Moon can be calculated by the application of the fundamental law of Newton. This law in fact allows us either to determine the motion of revolution of bodies in space if we know their masses or to calculate these masses when we know their motion. Now

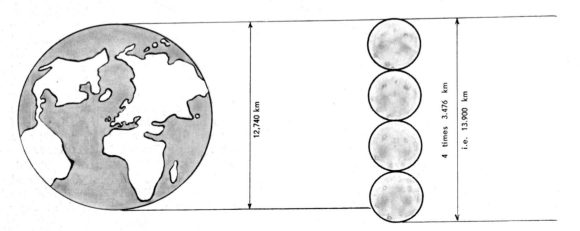

Comparison of terrestrial and lunar dimensions. — Photo 11. — *An outline of the British Isles superimposed on the north-west portion of the Moon.*

(Photo — Mount Wilson and Palomar Observatories — 100-inch telescope.)

Fig. 17. — Comparison of Moon and Earth diameters.

we have been able to establish the nature of the perturbations caused by the Moon on the Earth during its revolution around the Sun and from the divergencies found in this manner, it has been concluded that its mass is equal to 10/815 of that of our sphere, that is 74×10^{18} tons (Fig. 18). The lunar density which arises out of this result has been found equal to 3.33, that is about six-tenths of that of Earth. Gravity at the surface of our satellite is 6 times weaker than that on the Earth's equator ; this means that an object on the Moon, the weight of which (as measured by a spring balance and not a beam balance) would be 1 kg on Earth, would show no more on the same instrument than 166 g. A man arriving on the Moon would imagine himself six times stronger since with the same effort he could carry burdens which would have a mass six times greater.

Fig. 18. — Determination of the Moon's mass. When the Earth is at E_1, the Moon is at M_1 (i.e. full Moon) and its gravitational force tends to make the Earth move in a direction at right angles to its trajectory. The slight resultant displacement is only discernible with difficulty. But seven days later when the Earth ought to be at E_2 and the Moon at M_2 (now last quarter), the Moon's gravity is exerted in the same direction as the Earth's motion and this has the effect of causing the latter to accelerate slightly, taking up the position E_3. The opposite obviously takes place at first quarter. It is possible to calculate the additional trajectory covered by measuring the apparent displacement of the Sun in correlation with this phenomenon. The Sun appears at R_3 and not at R_2; the angle $R_2 S R_3$ is moreover minute, some six seconds of arc, but it corresponds to a value of the segment $E_2 E_3$, equal to about 1/81 of the Earth-Moon distance. From the magnitude of this perturbation it can be calculated that the mass of the Moon is equal to 1/81 of the mass of the Earth.

V

ROTATION OF THE MOON
ON ITS OWN AXIS

Simultaneous Revolution and Rotation

As the Moon makes a complete turn on its own axis in exactly the same time as it accomplishes a revolution around the Earth we never see any more of it than one and the same face. The following example will illustrate this phenomenon which often gives rise to confusion. On a cart is placed a sphere bearing certain distinctive marks and in particular twelve zones converging at the two points cut by its vertical axis. This vehicle makes a perfectly circular closed circuit in such a way that if it carries out a complete turn around an observer situated at the centre of the circle it constantly presents itself to the eyes of the latter with an identical aspect although against a variable background. As for the sphere the observer never sees any more of it than the same side, that is to say the same arrangement of zones. The reason, it is true, is not immediately apparent but it is quite simple : the sphere undergoes two simultaneous movements, a revolution and a rotation, the angular speeds of which are equal at every moment. In order to demonstrate this it is necessary

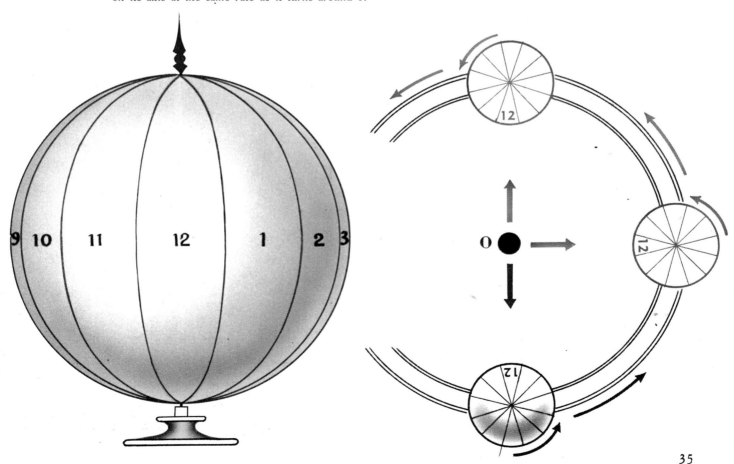

Fig. 19. — Simultaneous rotation and revolution. *If the sphere (shown on the left) is placed on a cart which describes a circle around point 0, an observer situated at this point will never see anything but the same face and consequently, the same sections (N°ˢ 9, 10, 11, 12, 1, 2 and 3). This is because the cart to which the sphere is rigidly fixed constantly turns on its axis at the same rate as it turns around 0.*

to make each motion independent, for example by placing the sphere on the cart but interposing a rotating platform mounted on a pivot like a compass needle. In the manner of a compass this platform is therefore supposed to keep permanently the same orientation whatever the position of the cart. From this it can be seen that when the cart moves the sphere participates in the revolution but not in the rotation, so that during the time of a complete circuit the observer sees the twelve zones drawn on the sphere move in front of him successively. What is now necessary to re-establish a situation in which the zones appear to be motionless ? Merely that the sphere be provided with some mechanism which makes it turn round its vertical axis in the same direction as the cart is turning and at a speed which is continuously equal to that of the revolution (Fig. 19).

The question quite naturally arises as to why the duration of revolution and rotation of the Moon are identical. We must immediately eliminate any hypothesis which suggests simple coincidence. In fact, if such had been the case at any time during the evolution of the planets the slightest perturbation — and causes of this are not lacking in the universe — would have modified this extraordinary chance and the displacement could only have become accentuated as time went on. It is therefore quite obvious that the identity in the duration of these two periodic motions can only be the result of the effect of one body on the other.

According to some, the Moon in the beginning was rather a fluid body turning relatively quickly on its axis. Owing to the attraction exercised on it by our sphere it was subject to tides similar to those occurring in our oceans but with an appreciably greater amplitude because of the considerably greater mass of the Earth. This continual constraint finally altered the shape of the Moon by causing an increase in the mass on one side which acted in the nature of a brake. The rotation period increased so that in the end it equalled that of one revolution of the Moon around the Earth.

Lunar Libration

Although the Moon continuously shows us the one face, we know rather more than half of the surface. In fact, the Moon seems to be subject to a slight but double oscillation simultaneously taking place on both the north-south and east-west axes. The first of these apparent motions can be compared to the rotation which

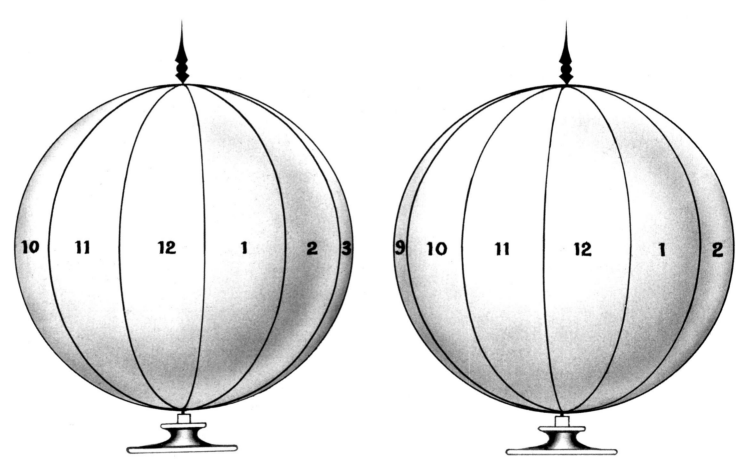

Fig. 20. — Effects of inequalities in the rotation and revolution velocities. If, by using the device of a moving platform mounted on the cart, the motions of rotation and revolution are made independent and if their angular velocities vary periodically, then the visible face of the sphere varies accordingly. Thus, when the speed of revolution is greater than the mean speed, new sections (or new parts of sections) appear on the right hand side. When on the contrary the speed of revolution is less than the mean, the new sections appear on the left, whilst those nearest to the right hand edge disappear.

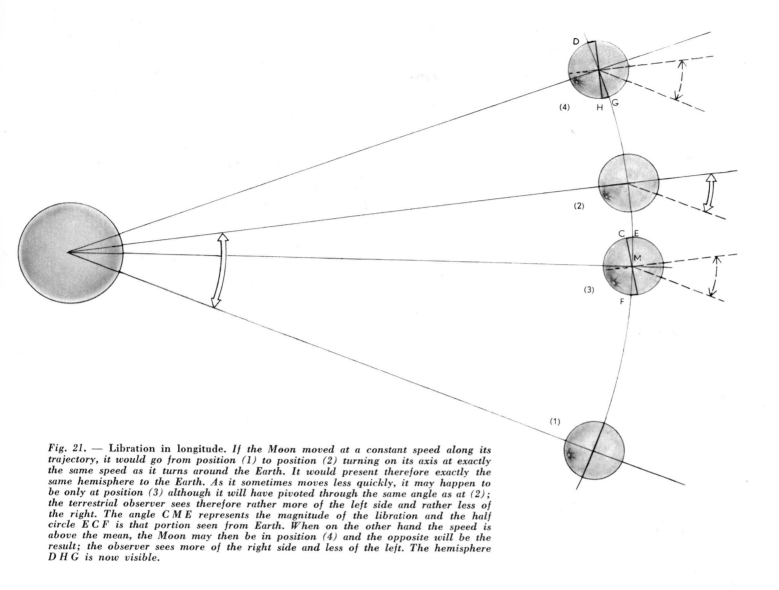

Fig. 21. — Libration in longitude. If the Moon moved at a constant speed along its trajectory, it would go from position (1) to position (2) turning on its axis at exactly the same speed as it turns around the Earth. It would present therefore exactly the same hemisphere to the Earth. As it sometimes moves less quickly, it may happen to be only at position (3) although it will have pivoted through the same angle as at (2); the terrestrial observer sees therefore rather more of the left side and rather less of the right. The angle C M E represents the magnitude of the libration and the half circle E C F is that portion seen from Earth. When on the other hand the speed is above the mean, the Moon may then be in position (4) and the opposite will be the result; the observer sees more of the right side and less of the left. The hemisphere D H G is now visible.

takes place alternately in one direction and the other by the weight of a torsion balance, though with an amplitude infinitely smaller of course. As for the second it gives us the impression that the Moon is in turn leaning towards the front and towards the back. As a consequence of these oscillations our field of visibility extends a little in the direction of each of the four cardinal lunar points. Three distinct causes are responsible for this state of affairs ; they are generally given the name of *libration*.

In conformity with the law of areas the Moon does not move in its elliptical orbit at constant speed ; on the other hand, the rotation to which it is subject is extremely regular. It follows from this, therefore, that the relationship between the angle through which it turns on its own axis in a given time and the arc which it describes in the same time is not constant. In order to understand the consequences of this deviation let us refer again to our previous example where a sphere is placed on a platform which acts like a compass ; we must suppose that it turns at a precisely constant speed completing the rotation in, say, 12 hours whilst the cart taking exactly 12 hours to complete its circuit travels at a variable speed. Under these new conditions the observer who watches the cart and its load no longer continually sees the same arrangement of zones ; the latter will seem to move sometimes towards the right, sometimes towards the left, so that new zones appear and disappear in turn on each side. The extent of visibility of these side zones will depend on the amplitude of the variations to which the speed of the cart is subject (Fig. 20). This is in fact what happens in the case of the Moon : during half its revolution round the Earth the left hand side is disclosed more fully and part of the right hand side disappears behind the limb ; during the other half the opposite takes place. This phenomenon, which is accentuated by the fact that our terrestrial observatory is not at the centre of a circular orbit, but at the focus of an elliptical orbit, is called *libration in longitude* ; its amplitude is 7° 54' (Fig. 21). Put in another way, two extreme portions of the Moon taking the shape of a crescent of

MARE CRISIUM

MARE CRISIUM

CLAVIUS

CLAVIUS

PLATO

PLATO

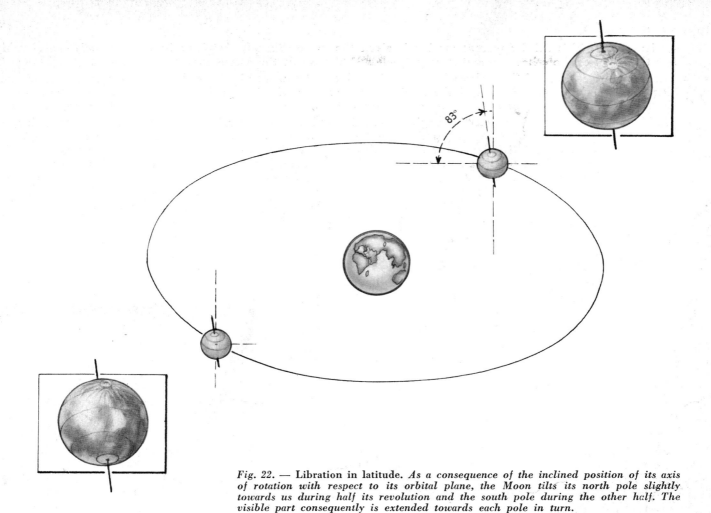

Fig. 22. — Libration in latitude. As a consequence of the inclined position of its axis of rotation with respect to its orbital plane, the Moon tilts its north pole slightly towards us during half its revolution and the south pole during the other half. The visible part consequently is extended towards each pole in turn.

Libration in longitude. — *Photos 12 and 13. — On photo N° 12 the lunar regions situated on the left of the Mare Crisium are clearly more extensive than on photo 13.*

(Photo : Mount Wilson and Palomar Observatories — 100-inch telescope.)
(Photo : Paris Observatory.)

Libration in latitude. — *Photos 14 and 15. — The Moon in photo 15 seems to lean towards us when compared with that in photo 14. The respective positions of the craters Clavius and Plato with respect to the upper and lower edges clearly show this phenomenon.*

(Photo : Paris Observatory.)
(Photo : Mount Wilson and Palomar Observatories — 100-inch telescope.)

approximately 8° of aperture are alternately visible and hidden on both sides of the north-south axis of our satellite. The second cause of libration occurs when the axis around which the Moon is turning is not perpendicular to the plane in which its orbit is situated. This situation is analogous to that concerning the axis of our own sphere although the inclination of our satellite is less accentuated ; whereas for the Earth the angle between the axis of rotation and the plane of the orbit is 67°, it is 83° for the Moon. Nevertheless, in the same way as the north and south poles of the Earth alternately lean towards the Sun during half the year, so the lunar poles lean alternately to the side of our sphere in turn during half the revolution of the Moon. This further apparent oscillation has an amplitude of 6° 50' ; it has received the name of *libration in latitude* since in this case the visible surface of our satellite is extended in latitude (Fig. 22).

Finally, in the third aspect of libration the Moon still seems to undergo a weak oscillation as a consequence of the rotation of the Earth. Since the distance separating us from the Moon is not infinite, an observer situated for example in Haiti does not see exactly the same surface of the Moon as another person observing at the same moment in Bangkok. This is simply due to the so-called *parallax effect,* a phenomenon which everybody witnesses when looking at a distant landscape from two points in succession separated laterally by some distance. Now the rotation of the Earth causes a displacement of the point from which the Moon is observed and thus a modification of its image. In the example cited earlier the second observer is, with respect to the Moon, in the position occupied by the first, 12 hours earlier. But during these 12 hours both of them have the impression that it is the Moon which pivots slightly on its axis. To this third apparent motion is given the name *diurnal libration* ; its amplitude is considerably less than that of the other two and it only reaches 1° 2' towards the east and west (Fig. 23).

The cumulative effect of these three librations is to let us know not half the total surface of the Moon but 59 per cent. Of this 41 per cent of the surface is perpetually visible and 18 per cent of the surface is some· times visible. Hence 41 per cent of the surface of our satellite remains unobservable from our sphere.

The frequency of these librations in longitude and latitude are linked with the sidereal revolution which, as we know, differs by about 2 days from the synodic revolution. The result of this is that at each lunation the phases take place with a different libration and this explains why a photograph representing, for example, the first quarter is not the same as another photograph taken exactly one or several lunations later. In order to accomplish this it would be necessary for the two photographs to be taken after a number of days equal to a whole multiple of the synodic and sidereal revolutions ; however, this condition would not be sufficient for it does not take account of the other motions of our satellite which will be discussed later on and which themselves modify the aspects under which we see the Moon throughout its different phases.

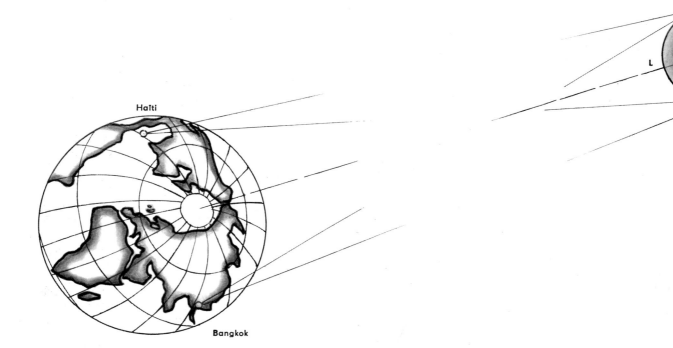

Fig. 23. — Diurnal libration. *As a result of the distance between Bangkok and Haiti, the lunar disc as seen from these places differs slightly. From Bangkok, the visible half of the Moon is defined by the half circle A L B. From Haiti, it is C L D. As the Earth turns on its axis, an observer who was at Bangkok at the beginning of the night will by the end of the night take up the position in space originally occupied by the observer at Haiti. During this time he will have the impression that the Moon oscillates slightly.*

VI

APPARENT TRAJECTORY
OF THE MOON

The way in which the Moon moves in the sky appears to be curiously freakish : it rises and sets each day at different hours, but the variation from one day to the next is far from being constant. The time it remains in the sky is likewise most variable ; in the space of 14 days it can vary from 8 to almost 16 hours. And the height which our satellite reaches in the celestial vault also varies periodically and with a relatively rapid rhythm.

All these fluctuations are due to variations in the orientation of the plane of the lunar orbit, some of which are real and others essentially apparent. Since the plane of the Moon's trajectory is very close to that of the ecliptic, it is essential to know right at the beginning that the ecliptic is the object of an apparent movement and the place it occupies in the sky is as much a function of the time of year as of a particular moment in the day.

Apparent Oscillation of the Terrestrial Globe

If our sphere rotated on an axis perpendicular to the plane of the ecliptic its annual motion would pass by unobserved by most mortals : the seasons would not exist, the duration of the day would be equal to that of the night, always and everywhere, and the apparent trajectory of the Sun would remain constantly parallel to itself at any point on the Earth. The seasonal variations are in fact entirely due to the inclination of the terrestrial axis to the plane of the ecliptic, and the annual revolution of the sphere merely has the effect of varying the angle at which the Sun's rays strike us. In fact, it seems as if the Earth instead of carrying out this revolution, remained at the same point in space but oscillated in one year about its proper centre with an amplitude of 23° 27', in such a way as alternately to incline the north and south poles towards the Sun. Consequently there is nothing to prevent us basing our discussion on this imaginary situation and considering that the angle formed in the plane of this oscillation by the terrestrial axis with the perpendicular to the Sun's rays constitutes a characteristic element of each day less of the year. It varies from — 23° 27' to + 23° 27', reaching these values at the solstices and becoming zero at the equinoxes (Fig. 24).

During the time taken by the daily rotation of the Earth all its points describe trajectories which are identical with the circles called « parallels ». If we consider the zenith of any place, it describes part of a cone, the apex of which is at the centre of the Earth. However, for an observer who participates in this motion but imagines that he is motionless, it is the sky above which moves, including everything connected with it such as the plane of the ecliptic itself. If he could then imagine this plane in the sky he would believe that it was driven by a gyroscopic motion, similar to that of the transverse flat surface of certain tops, being both an oscillation and a rotation. From this oscillation the observer has the impression that the plane of the ecliptic rises and sets successively throughout the day just like a hinged lid which is opened and closed in turn.

It can easily be demonstrated that the amplitude of this periodic movement is equal to double the imaginary characteristic angle defined above (Fig. 25). Being a function of the time of year it is at a maximum at the

Fig. 24. — Imaginary positions of the Earth with respect to the Sun. Without in any way upsetting the sequence of the seasons, we can imagine the Earth as fixed in space but oscillating about its centre O in one year, in the plane formed by the Earth's north-south axis and the centre of the Sun. The angle q, made by the oscillating axis with the line perpendicular to the Sun's rays, is then the characteristic element of the particular day under discussion; it varies constantly and its amount extends from —23° 27' to +23° 27' from one solstice to the next.

At the summer solstice

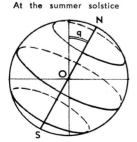

At the equinoxes

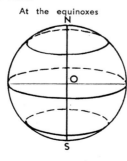

At the winter solstice

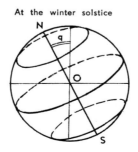

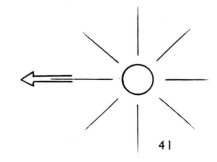

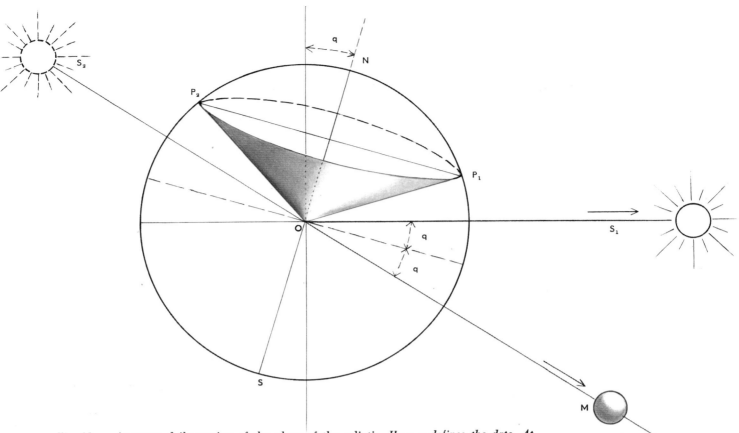

Fig. 25. — *Apparent daily motion of the plane of the ecliptic. Here q defines the date. At noon an observer situated at P₁ sees the Sun in the direction O S₁. Twelve hours later, at midnight, the observer is at P₂ having described in space a portion of the upturned cone whose apex is the centre of the Earth. However, he has the impression that he has not moved. For him, it is the Sun which has gone round the Earth, has disappeared below the horizon and is in the direction O S₂. If the period under discussion is at full Moon, the Moon is 12 hours behind the Sun in its journey around the Earth and is therefore situated on the opposite side of the Earth, that is to say, on the extension of the straight line S₂ O and the observer at P₁ sees it in the direction O M. The fundamental rules of geometry show that the angle S₁ O M, the apparent angle of displacement of the plane of the ecliptic, is equal to twice q.*

solstices (46° 54'), and zero at the equinoxes. In short, only twice throughout the year, on the 21st March and the 22nd September, does the plane of the ecliptic remain in the same apparent position throughout the whole day.

Lunar Trajectories in Summer and Winter

In order to understand easily how the apparent lunar trajectory appears at different times in the year, it is necessary as a first approximation to suppose that our satellite moves along the plane of the ecliptic. This is perfectly reasonable since the angle made by this plane with that of the lunar orbit is very small (5° 8' 43") and the effect of this displacement can be explained separately. When the Moon is new, it is situated in the same direction as the Sun : this means that in summer it climbs very high in the sky whilst in winter it remains close to the horizon. On the other hand, when it is full it lags approximately 12 hours behind the Sun during which lapse of time the plane of the ecliptic passes precisely from one extreme apparent position to the other ; the trajectories of the two bodies are consequently very much separated. The contrast is obviously greatest at the time of the solstices, and therefore in summer we never see full Moons high in the sky, whilst in winter we can look on them in all their splendour. For an analogous reason it is during the spring equinox that the first quarters reach their maximum height whilst it is during the autumnal equinox that the last quarters reach their highest culmination.

In certain regions of the Earth the lunar trajectory presents interesting features. At the equator, for example, at the time of the equinoxes the Sun and the Moon both cross the sky in the vertical east-west plane whatever may be the phase of the Moon ; at the solstices, on the other hand, the trajectories of the Sun and the full Moon lean 23° 27' towards the north or south, and this particular case immediately demonstrates the maximum value of the separation (46° 54') between the apparent limits of the plane of the ecliptic. In the polar regions the trajectory followed by the Moon is a real godsend to explorers. During the winter solstice, in fact, when the Sun has reached its lowest point below the horizon and when the ice-cap is consequently plunged into darkness of long duration, the Moon reaches its greatest height. The light which it then gives out and which the whiteness of the snows makes even more brilliant provides understandably an inestimable compensation. At the poles themselves the Moon describes a trajectory very close to the horizon which makes it remain constantly visible during half its period of revolution.

Ascending and Descending Nodes

The consequences arising out of the displacement between the planes of the lunar orbit and of the ecliptic are immediately apparent if we consider the apparent trajectories of the Sun and the Moon. The two circles which form them cut each other at two points called the nodes and the straight line which joins these points, that is to say the line of intersection of the orbital planes, is called the *line of the nodes*. The Moon, therefore, remains below the plane of the ecliptic during half its revolution and above this plane during the other half. It crosses the *ascending node* whilst going from the lower region to the upper and it passes the *descending node* in the opposite direction. The plane of the lunar orbit does not always keep a fixed position in space. It is also the subject of a gyroscopic motion so that the line of the nodes does not remain orientated in a changeless way. It turns in an opposite direction to the motion of the revolution of the Moon and makes a complete circle in 18 years 224 days (Fig. 26).

The inclination of the lunar orbit and its gyroscopic motion do not modify our former conclusions except quantitatively. In order to know the height to which our satellite rises in the sky at any particular moment it is necessary to combine the angle made by the planes of the equator and the ecliptic with that resulting from the separation between the planes of the ecliptic and the lunar orbit. As this is based on spherical

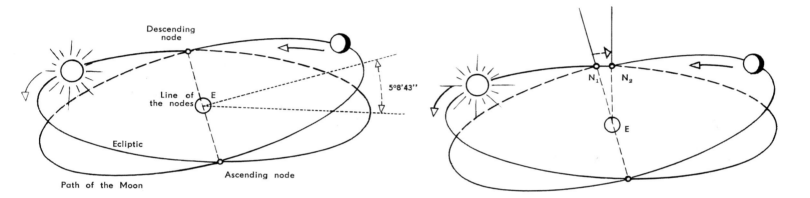

trigonometry the problem is not a question of simple addition for we must take account of the orientation of the points of intersection of these planes. In fact, the resulting angle can either be greater or smaller than that which gives the height of the Sun. Its maximum value is reached when the vernal equinox, that is to say the point on the ecliptic passed by the Sun when it crosses the equator from south to north, coincides with the ascending node ; the Moon then reaches a height of 23° 27' plus 5° 9', that is 28° 36'. Its minimum value corresponds on the contrary to the moment when the vernal equinox coincides with the descending node ; the Moon in this case only reaches a height of 23° 27' minus 5° 9', that is 18° 18'. Whatever it may be, this shows that the divergency in the celestial latitude is greater for the Moon than for the Sun.

Still other causes exist which accentuate the irregularity of the lunar trajectory but it is impossible to mention them all. In fact, over a thousand have been discovered and this fantastic figure is brought about because the Moon practically never finds itself under identical conditions. Its position varies continually either in relation to the Earth or to other planets and the Sun, and this at each instant modifies the action exercised on it by neighbouring heavenly bodies. Although most of these perturbations have very little importance, astronomers must nevertheless take note of several hundreds of them when they are considering the establishment of lunar ephemerides.

Amongst these secondary motions of the Moon there is one which has a certain importance particularly for those who compute the occurrence of eclipses : this is the rotation in its own plane of the ellipse constituting the lunar orbit. Its axes in fact turn in the same direction as the Moon and the duration of a cycle in 8 years 10 days (Fig. 27).

Yet another cause of irregularity which cannot be neglected is the variation of the inclination of the plane of the lunar orbit. The angle given above, 5° 8' 43", is in reality only an average value. During a period of 173 days it oscillates between two extreme values, namely 5° 0' 1" and 5° 17' 35".

Fig. 26. — Apparent trajectories of the Sun and Moon and the regression of the nodes. *The first diagram represents the apparent orbits of the Sun and Moon if there were no gyroscopic motion of the Moon's orbital plane. The second shows this phenomenon and in consequence the regression of the nodes. A complete circle of the line of the nodes takes 18 years 224 days.*

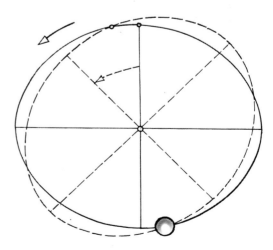

Fig. 27. — Rotation of the lunar orbit in its own plane. *Every 8 years 10 days the lunar trajectory in the shape of an ellipse makes a complete circle about its centre and in its own plane.*

The Rising and the Setting of the Moon

If we look up in a calendar, during a month, the daily hours of the rising and the setting of the Moon as well as its transit of the meridian and if we construct a graph of these points and join them up, we obtain three curves which have a striking appearance (Fig. 28). Whilst the two outer curves are very wavy the third, that is to say the one concerning the transit of the meridian by the Moon, is almost a straight line. This indicates that the lapse of time separating two consecutive transits is practically constant, a conclusion which can be demonstrated without difficulty. The moment of transit is the time when the Moon crosses in the sky the plane of a great circle in which are comprised the point of observation and the two terrestrial poles. In other words it is the moment when our satellite is in mid-course and consequently in the highest position in the heavens ; this moment is independent of the apparent position of the plane of the lunar orbit. The time which separates one transit from the next is a function of the speed of rotation of the Earth on its axis which is extremely regular, and of the motion of a revolution of the Moon which is not strictly uniform ; the middle curve of our diagram is not, therefore, strictly a straight-line.

As for the sinuous aspects of the two other curves, this can best be explained by comparing these with curves showing sunrise and sunset. As we know, it is the inclination of the plane of the ecliptic to that of the equator which causes the daily advance of the hour of sunrise and the retardation of that of sunset for half the year and which gives rise to the opposite effect during the other half. Likewise it is the inclination of the plane of the lunar orbit to that of the terrestrial equator which causes the variation in the hours of rising and setting of our satellite. All the same, there is an enormous difference between these two phenomena when we consider the duration of the cycle : whilst the Sun takes 365 days to complete its cycle the Moon only takes 29. The daily divergence between the rising and setting of the Moon is therefore greater and the rhythm of this variation is considerably faster. Since these divergencies combine with the Moon's daily time lag, the latter is sometimes increased and sometimes reduced.

Finally, just as in the case of solar phenomena, the amplitude of the variations increases in magnitude as the country where they are produced is further from the equator. At a latitude of 40° for example, the daily time lag of moonrise varies between 13 and 80 minutes. In more northerly countries this divergence increases still more and there arise certain occasions when the minimum value becomes only a few minutes. This is exactly the case of the « Harvest Moon », well-known in the north of England and much appreciated by country folk : the September Moon, round about its full state, rises for several consecutive days at almost the same time, that is to say at the moment when the Sun sets ; thus daylight is prolonged to the great satisfaction of harvesters.

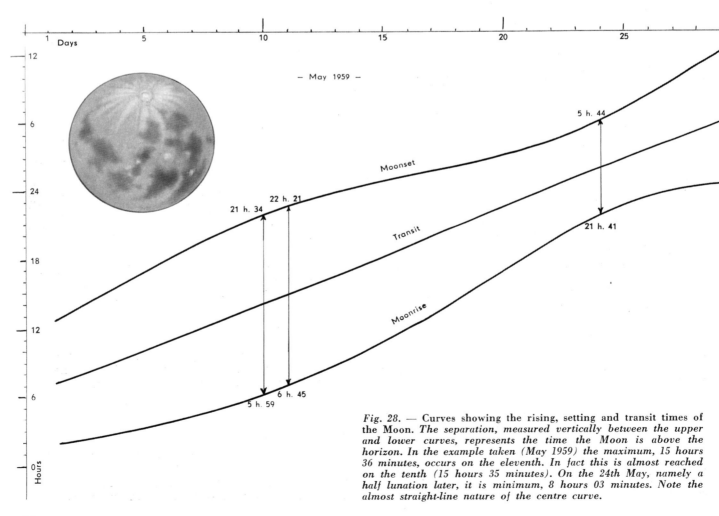

Fig. 28. — Curves showing the rising, setting and transit times of the Moon. *The separation, measured vertically between the upper and lower curves, represents the time the Moon is above the horizon. In the example taken (May 1959) the maximum, 15 hours 36 minutes, occurs on the eleventh. In fact this is almost reached on the tenth (15 hours 35 minutes). On the 24th May, namely a half lunation later, it is minimum, 8 hours 03 minutes. Note the almost straight-line nature of the centre curve.*

VII

THE MECHANISM
OF THE ECLIPSES

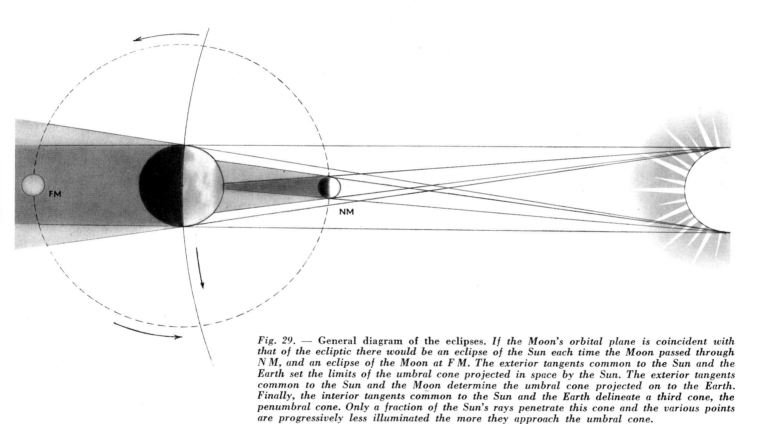

Fig. 29. — General diagram of the eclipses. *If the Moon's orbital plane is coincident with that of the ecliptic there would be an eclipse of the Sun each time the Moon passed through N M, and an eclipse of the Moon at F M. The exterior tangents common to the Sun and the Earth set the limits of the umbral cone projected in space by the Sun. The exterior tangents common to the Sun and the Moon determine the umbral cone projected on to the Earth. Finally, the interior tangents common to the Sun and the Earth delineate a third cone, the penumbral cone. Only a fraction of the Sun's rays penetrate this cone and the various points are progressively less illuminated the more they approach the umbral cone.*

If the Moon's orbit were in the plane of the ecliptic, the three bodies, Sun, Earth and Moon, would find themselves in a straight line at each occasion of *syzygy* (the name given to the time of a new or a full Moon). At the time of the new Moon our satellite would interpose itself exactly between the Earth and the Sun and would mask the latter each time, whilst at full Moon our sphere, being exactly between the Sun and the Moon, would plunge the latter into its shade. Throughout each lunation there would therefore always be two eclipses, one of the Sun and one of the Moon (Fig. 29).

In fact, as the orbital planes of the Moon and the Earth are not coincident such alignments, although occurring at precisely determined intervals, are rare. For the most part, when the Moon is new it passes in the sky either a little above or a little below the Sun, never being further away, however, than 5° 8', which is the angle made between the planes of the two orbits.

Total and Partial Eclipses

Since the alignment of the three bodies constitutes the fundamental condition for an eclipse, it is necessary in every case for the Moon to be in the plane of the ecliptic (indeed the origin of this word comes from this requisite). This means that the only possible position is on the line of the nodes; the Moon cuts this line 25 times a year but during the same time the Sun only cuts it twice, once at each extremity, so that their meeting cannot be very frequent. If on the one hand we consider the relatively great apparent dimensions of the Sun and the Moon, and on the other hand the smallness of the angle between the two orbital planes, we must agree that even if the centres of these three bodies are not accurately placed on the same straight line, a phenomenon of occultation may be produced but only in part. This case can arise, for example, if the new Moon, although passing in the sky slightly to the side of the Sun, is nevertheless sufficiently close to it to mask a portion. Astronomers have therefore been led to define two sorts of phenomena : they state that the eclipse is *total* when the masked body disappears entirely, that is to say, according to conditions, the Sun behind the Moon or the Moon in the shade projected by the Earth. The eclipse is said to be *partial* when even at the moment of the greatest phase a part of the eclipsed body still remains visible (Fig. 30).

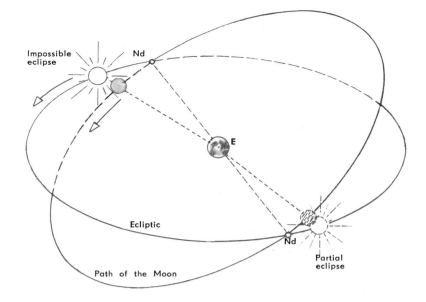

Fig. 30. — Possible and impossible eclipses. *The positions of the Moon and the Sun (top left) show that the new Moon occurs too long after our satellite has passed the descending node; no eclipse is possible. The encounter shown bottom right, occurs sufficiently close to the ascending node for the Sun to be partially eclipsed by the Moon.*

Relative Frequency of the Eclipses of the Sun and the Moon

Eclipses of the Sun occur more frequently than eclipses of the Moon and this is explained if we examine the respective chances that each has of occurring. To this effect let us consider the cone which circumscribes the Sun and the Earth in space and let us distinguish the following two parts : the lower portion, that which lies between the two bodies, and the upper, that which extends from the Earth to the point of the cone. There is an eclipse of the Sun when the Moon penetrates the zone in the first portion, whilst there is an eclipse of the Moon when our satellite enters the second. As the width of the cone in these two places has a relationship of about 4 to 3 it is precisely in this proportion that the two types of eclipse occur (Fig. 31).

However, we must not be misled by this last conclusion for it seems to contradict our experience that eclipses of the Sun appear to be rarer than eclipses of the Moon. Therefore it must be stated that the former are only ever observable in an extremely limited region of the Earth, whilst the latter can be seen simultaneously from all the points of a hemisphere. This important point which differentiates the two types of eclipse requires some explanation.

For an eclipse of the Sun the inhabitants of the various countries of the world are in the same situation as a group of people who, although somewhat separated from each other, are looking at a very distant countryside : for example a chain of mountains on the horizon. An aeroplane flying one or two kilometres away from us passing in front of the chain might cause one mountain to disappear suddenly from the sight of one person. Another person, quite near to the latter, would perhaps notice a partial occultation at the same moment and even a complete disappearance at a slightly different instant, but other people much further away from the two first mentioned would never see the aeroplane hide the mountain in question. This exactly parallels an eclipse of the Sun : even if it is total it only appears as such along a relatively narrow band of the Earth's surface ; it is partially visible from some part or other of this band in an appreciably wider region but for the rest of the world it does not occur at all.

For a lunar eclipse we must consider quite a different comparison and imagine, for example, the distant mountain chain illuminated in the first place by the Sun and then disappearing in the shade of a large cloud. The situation is now very different : the object which received the light is brusquely deprived of it and this phenomenon is of course perceivable at the same instant by all the groups of people who observe it. This is the situation during an eclipse of the Moon which occurs at the same moment for the half of the world from which our satellite is visible.

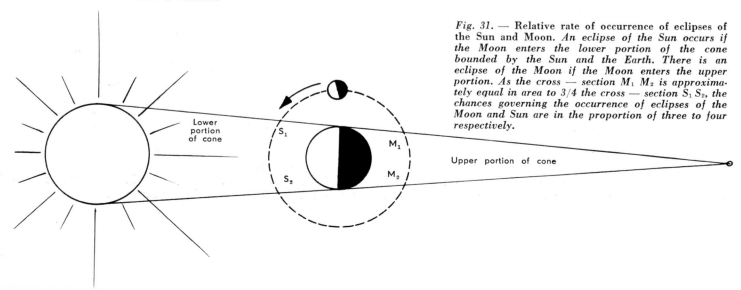

Fig. 31. — Relative rate of occurrence of eclipses of the Sun and Moon. *An eclipse of the Sun occurs if the Moon enters the lower portion of the cone bounded by the Sun and the Earth. There is an eclipse of the Moon if the Moon enters the upper portion. As the cross — section $M_1 M_2$ is approximately equal in area to 3/4 the cross — section $S_1 S_2$, the chances governing the occurrence of eclipses of the Moon and Sun are in the proportion of three to four respectively.*

Prediction of Eclipses

The ancients saw baleful signs in eclipses ; the fear which their occurrence occasioned was as deep as the admiration in which they held wise men capable of predicting them. Thanks to the observations carried out throughout the centuries by men of science who had preceded them, some astronomers of antiquity had managed to establish empirically a very simple law which stated the periodic return of certain eclipses. Nevertheless they limited their predictions merely to eclipses of the Moon, for they found it impossible to determine the regions of visibility of the eclipses of the Sun and very probably did not know that the latter repeated themselves in the same way. In our day, astronomers know practically all the elements governing the motion of bodies and they can consequently calculate with very great accuracy the time at which eclipses of all types take place. Strictly speaking this calculation is not difficult but it is infinitely complex when we consider the multiplicity of factors which have to be taken into account. To determine the periodicity of an eclipse we must calculate the lapse of time necessary to bring the Sun and Moon into identical positions relative to us on Earth. As our satellite is the object of several cyclic motions the required periodicity is simply the smallest whole multiple of all the cycles under consideration.

Since the fundamental condition of the repetition of an eclipse is the return of the Moon to a clearly defined phase, the first cycle to be considered is the lunation or synodic revolution, the duration of which is 29 days 12 hours and 44 minutes or as a decimal fraction 29.5306 days. The second cycle is that which determines the passage of the Moon on the line of the nodes ; this would be the same as the sidereal revolution if the line in question remained orientated in the sky in a changeless way. But as it is itself displaced (we have seen above that it makes a complete circle in 18 years 224 days), and as its movement is retrograde, the time which separates two consecutive passages of the Moon to the same node is slightly shorter. It is equal to 27 days 5 hours and 5 minutes or as a decimal fraction 27.2122 days, an interval which has been called the *draconitic revolution.*

Since the distance between the Earth and the Moon varies periodically because the lunar orbit is elliptical, a third cycle has to be considered which gives the periodical return of our satellite to the same distance from our sphere. Once again, in this case the period under consideration is not a sidereal revolution since the axes of the ellipse themselves turn a complete circle in their own plane, taking rather less than 9 years ; and since here the motion is in the same direction, the time interval which separates two consecutive passages of the Moon to its perigee is this time rather longer. This has been called the *anomalistic revolution ;* it is 27 days 13 hours and 18 minutes, or as a decimal fraction 27.5545 days.

The distance of the Earth to the Sun also varies periodically since the terrestrial orbit is equally elliptical and this variation must be taken into consideration along with the others. It is therefore necessary to introduce into the calculation a fourth cycle which determines the periodical return of the Sun to the same distance from the Earth, that is quite simply the *year.*

If we followed strictly the rule of the smallest whole multiple, we would obtain colossal numbers for these periods of the repetition of an eclipse. It is not, in fact, difficult to calculate that in the case where only the first two conditions are taken into consideration the smallest whole number corresponding to the question is a fabulous one ; the solution is simple : 272,122 synodic revolutions or 295,306 draconitic revolutions which corresponds to almost 22,000 years !

The Saros

Fortunately we can make do with an approximate solution by admitting, for example, that the cycle of repetition does not imply the reappearance of the eclipse in the same zone of visibility. This means we can simplify the relationship $\frac{272122}{295306}$ by replacing it by another ordinary fraction of appreciably equivalent value but having smaller terms. The theory of continuous fractions allows us in this respect to find a series of approximate solutions of increasing accuracy, amongst which we can choose those which represent an acceptable precision.

By developing as a continuous fraction the ratio $\frac{272122}{295306}$, we obtain a series of ordinary fractions of which the following are useful : $\frac{47}{51}$, $\frac{223}{242}$, $\frac{939}{1019}$, etc., fractions in which numerators and denominators respectively represent the number of synodic and draconitic revolutions of a cycle corresponding to intervals of time which are appreciably equivalent. The approximation given by the first of these fractions is rather rough and unacceptable ; the second corresponds to a system of prediction used in antiquity, the *saros* of the Chaldeans. It can in fact be proved that 223 synodic revolutions are equivalent in time — almost to the hour — to 242 draconitic revolutions and this represents a cycle of 18 years 11 days and 8 hours.

How does it come about that this period can be stated so exactly when we have only considered the first two conditions in its calculation ? According to what we have said, would it not be necessary to look for the smallest whole multiple of all revolutions, synodic, draconitic and anomalistic as well as years ? Here we have the intervention of a mysterious stroke of fortune which has simplified things remarkably and which is even more extraordinary since it is double. The fact is that 223 synodic revolutions are not only equivalent to a complete number of draconitic revolutions but also to a whole number of anomalistic revolutions, in fact 239, and once again almost to the hour. The third condition, that which demands the return to the same value of the Earth-Moon distance, is therefore resolved. Furthermore, as the saros almost exactly comprises a complete number of years — within almost 11 days — the fourth condition which concerns the Earth-Sun distance is likewise equally satisfied. Though it seemed that the repetition of an eclipse would take place only after an extremely long interval, two prodigious coincidences bring the period to less than 20 years and make the saros a cycle of considerable interest although defying all the laws of logic.

The Number of Eclipses in a given Period

If a particular eclipse is repeated every 18 years it is very evident that during this time others take place which are repeated according to the same rule. The calculation of the number of eclipses which can happen in a given time, say, for example, in a year, presents moreover an instructive problem. This can easily by resolved if we know the maximum distance separating the Sun from a node for an eclipse to be possible. With regard to eclipses of the Sun it has been calculated that the divergence can reach 18° 30' and that if it is no greater than 10° the eclipse is total. The result of this is that in reality the points in space where the Sun and the Moon must meet in order to bring about an eclipse are not exclusively the two nodes but two arcs of the ecliptic of 37° aperture extending from 18° 30' on either side of these nodes (Fig. 32).

Every 29 days the Moon travels along each of the two arcs once, whilst the Sun is on this section. As the Sun needs 365 days to cover the 360° of the ecliptic, it advances practically 1° per day and therefore takes 37 days to move along each arc. It follows inevitably that while the Sun is describing an arc, the Moon must pass by at least once, and this explains why there is always a minimum of two eclipses of the Sun per year (one on each arc). However, if the Moon reaches an arc very soon after the Sun, it has time to come round again, passing the Sun once more at the other end of this particular arc. Thus the number of eclipses can be four in a year (two on each arc). In 1964, for example, there will be eclipses on 14th January, 10th June, 9th July and 4th December. Finally, if the first eclipse takes place before the 11th January, five eclipses of the Sun then arise in the same year. Such an event happened in 1935, namely on the 5th January, 3rd February, 30th June, 30th July and 25th December ; these dates clearly show that, four of the five eclipses must necessarily be grouped in twos with an interval of a lunation between each component of the pair.

For eclipses of the Moon, the two arcs of the ecliptic where the Sun and the Moon must be to bring about the phenomenon, are less extended. A calculation analogous to the preceding shows that there can be at a maximum three eclipses of the Moon, but that there may very well be none at all. Summing up, a year can have at a maximum seven eclipses which are shared according to one of the following formulae : either four eclipses of the Sun and three of the Moon, or five of the Sun and two of the Moon. The minimum in a year is two eclipses — both of the Sun.

Magnitude

In order to define the degree of importance of a partial eclipse, that is to say to state accurately how far this eclipse approaches totality, astronomers employ the term *magnitude*. This notion which is usually given in the form of a decimal fraction such as 0.3, 0.75, 0.87, easily leads to confusion. In fact, contrary to what one is instinctively inclined to believe, it does not represent for the eclipsed body the proportion of the visible *surface* which has been obscured but the fraction of the *diameter* which is hidden at the moment of maximum obscuration.

When it is a question of a partial eclipse of the Sun, for example, the magnitude is said to be equal to 0.5 if the Moon happens to hide half the solar diameter ; it is not difficult to work out that at this moment the portion of the solar surface masked by the Moon is only equal to somewhat more than a third of the total surface.

For an eclipse of the Moon the definition is somewhat more complex : the magnitude represents the fraction of the lunar diameter hidden by the shadow but this notion is extended to total eclipses ; now as the disc of the shadow has a diameter greater than that of the Moon it can happen that magnitudes are greater than unity. The maximum which can be reached takes place when the centre of the Moon and the shadow are coincident and when the correspondence between the section of the shadow cone and the lunar surface is maximum. It is then equal to 1.89 (Figs. 33 and 35).

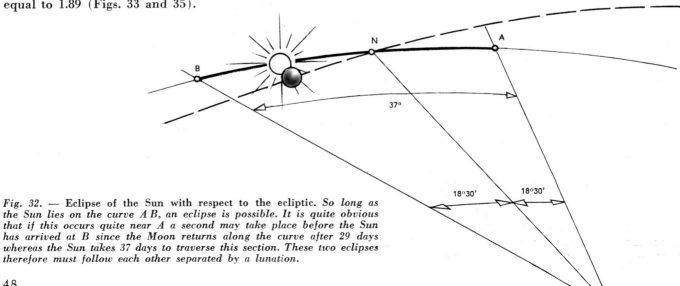

Fig. 32. — Eclipse of the Sun with respect to the ecliptic. So long as the Sun lies on the curve A B, an eclipse is possible. It is quite obvious that if this occurs quite near A a second may take place before the Sun has arrived at B since the Moon returns along the curve after 29 days whereas the Sun takes 37 days to traverse this section. These two eclipses therefore must follow each other separated by a lunation.

VIII

ECLIPSES OF THE MOON

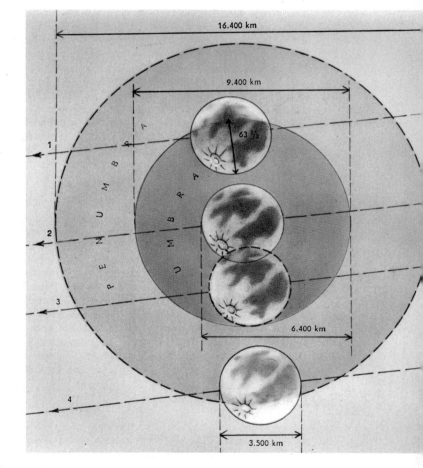

Fig. 33. — The three types of eclipses of the Moon. If the Moon follows the upper trajectory on the diagram, the eclipse is only partial. At the time of its maximum obscuration 63 % of its diameter is in total shadow and the magnitude of the eclipse is therefore in this case 0.63.
The second trajectory passes exactly through the middle of the umbra. The eclipse is total and its magnitude greater than 1. If we allow the same definition for the latter as for the partial eclipse, namely the ratio between the « eclipsed edge to shadow edge » distance and the apparent lunar diameter, its value will be given by the fraction $\frac{6400}{3500} = 1.83$. This numerical example almost corresponds therefore to the case of maximum eclipse (1.89), which occurs when the Moon is at perigee during eclipse.
If the Moon followed the third trajectory, the magnitude would be exactly unity as is clearly seen in the diagram.
Finally, the fourth trajectory is that of a penumbral eclipse.

Umbra and Penumbra

If there were spread out behind the Moon, a gigantic light-coloured cloth considerably greater in surface area than the Moon, we would see this screen lit up by the Sun during the night. About the time of full Moon a huge black circular patch would appear, the *umbra* of the Earth, surrounded by a darkish ring, although appreciably less black, called the *penumbra*. As the Sun is not a point source of light there is in fact a zone only partially affected by the passage of the Earth in front of the Sun ; it only receives a part of the Sun's rays and the closer its various points are to the true umbra, the less illuminated they are (Fig. 29).

As a consequence of the respective dimensions of the Sun and the Moon, the cone of the umbra which our sphere projects in space has a total length of almost 1,400,000 kilometres, that is 217 times the radius of the Earth. At the distance of the Moon its section (that is the dark patch which would be thrown on to the screen) has a diameter of almost 9 400 kilometres, that is 2.7 times that of the Moon. Geometrically speaking, our satellite can therefore be completely inscribed within it with ease. As for the cone of the penumbra which contrary to the umbra opens out as it approaches the Moon, it has a diameter of 16,400 kilometres at the same distance which represents approximately 4.8 times that of the Moon.

These few data make it immediately apparent why the transit of the Moon in the zones of the umbra and penumbra is relatively long, this being besides one of the essential points of difference between the eclipses of the Moon and the Sun. At a maximum 4 hours are necessary for the Moon to cross both zones and approximately 2 hours to cross only the umbra.

There are three types of eclipses of the Moon which are distinguished by the path followed by our satellite through the zones in question. As stated previously, the full Moon passes for most of the time in the sky either a little above or a little below the circles of the umbra and the penumbra. When the lunar trajectory crosses these circles, coming sufficiently close to their common centre for the lunar disc to be entirely engulfed in shade, then there is a *total eclipse*. But if our satellite penetrates into the umbra without being completely obscured, that is to say if its trajectory is too far removed from the centre of the umbra, it is a *partial eclipse*. Finally, if the Moon only crosses the annular zone the eclipse is called *umbral*. Whatever the type of eclipse, the Moon must naturally pass through the penumbra before and after it crosses the umbra. Therefore a total eclipse comprises multiple phases which can be detailed as follows : entry into the penumbra, entry into the umbra, commencement, middle and end of the phase of totality, exit from the umbra, exit from the penumbra (Fig. 33). Umbral eclipses, which are only of interest to astronomers, are impossible to observe without the aid of special instruments — that is why they are not announced to the public — but it is important to know that if they were taken into account, the number of total eclipses of the Moon would be the same as that for eclipses of the Sun.

For the inhabitants of the northern hemisphere the Moon moves from right to left in the sky so that they would see the shadow circle invade the lunar disc from left to right. In reality, the cone of the umbra advances in the same direction as our satellite but much more slowly ; consequently it is an optical illusion which gives the impression that the shadow moves in the opposite direction in front of a motionless Moon.

The Appearance of the Eclipsed Moon

Immediately after the contact between the Moon and the umbra the circular spot which constitutes the latter progressively covers our satellite, but the eclipsed portion does not disappear completely to the point of merging into the black sky ; first of all, its colour is grey, turning gradually to a brown, and during the total eclipse it generally becomes a very dark reddish brown. This illumination appears quite unexpectedly since at this moment the Moon receives no light from the Sun. In fact this is not quite true, for if no ray from the Sun can reach it directly others are capable of doing so indirectly ; it is the atmosphere surrounding our sphere which is responsible for this curious phenomenon. Acting like a lens, it bends the light rays, concentrating them towards the Moon, and this refraction to which there is added a certain absorption explains the characteristic colouration of the eclipsed body from which are excluded blue and violet tones. Moreover, the colours which adorn our satellite during a total eclipse are of the greatest interest to astronomers for they provide precious information on the composition of our atmosphere. The following example is indisputable proof. In the month of August 1883 the fantastic volcanic eruption of Krakatoa occurred, the smoke and dust of which profoundly affected the terrestrial atmosphere. Now during the total eclipses which took place in 1884 and 1885 the hue assumed by the Moon was of an exceptionable dark grey ; nothing could demonstrate better than this that the Sun's rays which indirectly lit up our satellite had effectively crossed the terrestrial atmosphere still charged with impurities.

Lunar Eclipses Seen from the Moon

One of the most astonishing spectacles which man will see when he manages to reach our satellite will be that which he will contemplate from his new observatory whilst his Earth-bound colleagues are watching a total eclipse of the Moon. For him, this will be a total eclipse of the Sun of great duration and of enormously striking appearance. The disc of the Earth masking the Sun will be the object of his astonishment not only because its surface is 3½ times greater than that of the lunar disc, but also because during the eclipse our atmosphere will surround it with a luminous ring, being illuminated from behind. Besides, as we have just seen, the darkness in which the lunar explorer will be plunged will not be complete, and the weak copper-tinted illumination which will come from this ring will no doubt give to the setting a supremely fairy-like character. The traveller on the Moon will also possess another advantage compared to us ; whilst we can see practically nothing of an umbral eclipse, he on the contrary will witness a very visible celestial phenomenon which will be nothing less than a partial eclipse of the Sun. In fact, the zones of the umbra and the penumbra on the Moon correspond to terrestrial regions where the eclipse of the Sun is respectively total and partial.

An Eclipse of the Moon at Sunset

It can happen that at the moment when the Moon rises it can be seen already eclipsed whilst the Sun is only on the point of setting. There is, however, a double explanation for this apparently very unlikely event since the alignment of the three bodies cannot occur under such circumstances. The first cause of it is the refraction introduced by the terrestrial atmosphere ; as they cross the layer of air which surrounds us, the light rays bend in slightly towards the Earth so that in a general way we perceive a little above the horizon objects which in reality are below. In the case under consideration the Sun and the Moon which can be seen simultaneously in diametrically opposed directions are in fact both below the horizon. The second explanation depends on the fact that as the cone of the umbra is relatively large, the Moon can be immersed by it without its centre necessarily being aligned with the centres of the Earth and the Sun. In any case very few people will have the occasion to witness this strange event ; they must in fact be in the region where the eclipse takes place precisely at the moment of sunset. Moreover the duration of this phenomenon never exceeds a few minutes. On the 15th February, 1887, such an event took place in Paris ; whilst the Sun was not due to set until 17 hours 39 minutes, the Moon had risen at 17 h 29 min, already totally eclipsed. On the 4th December 1880, the same situation occurred and in even more exceptional circumstances : moonrise took place at 16 hours whilst the sunset did not take place until 2 minutes later ; now at this moment it was almost the middle of a total eclipse as this lasted from 15 h 3 min to 16 h 33 min.

IX

ECLIPSES OF THE SUN

The Different Types of Solar Eclipses

Amongst all the coincidences that one can meet in astronomy one of the most extraordinary is the similarity which exists between the apparent surface areas of the Sun and the Moon. It is therefore quite understandable that the ancients considered these two heavenly bodies to be of the same nature and the same dimensions. In fact, the Sun has a diameter 400 times greater than that of the Moon but this disproportion is counterbalanced by the fact that it is likewise 400 times further off. Besides, chance has ordered things in such a fashion that the slight variations which affect the distances that separate us from these two bodies make the apparent dimensions of the Sun sometimes slightly greater than those of the Moon and sometimes rather smaller. During the time the Earth passes from *perihelion* (the point on its trajectory the closest to the Sun)

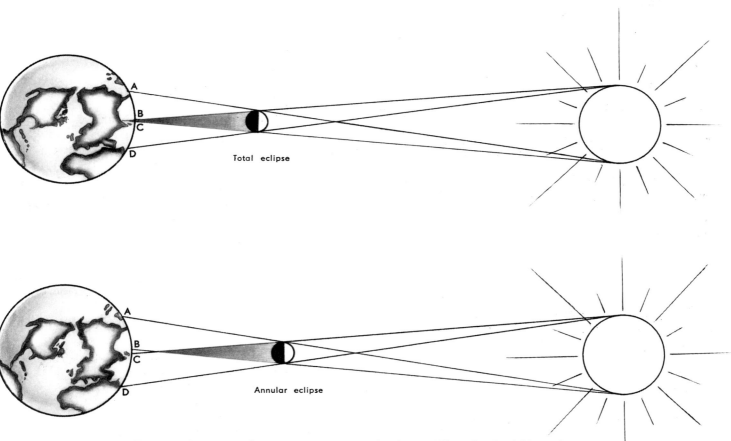

Total eclipse

Annular eclipse

Fig. 34. — Diagram showing extreme cases of eclipses. When the Earth-Moon distance is least and the Earth-Sun distance greatest, the apparent lunar disc is at its maximum whilst that of the Sun is at its minimum. The apex of the cone of shadow lies within the interior of the Earth and the eclipse is total in the zone B C and partial at A B and C D. When on the contrary the Earth-Moon and Earth-Sun distances are at a maximum and minimum respectively, the opposite is the case and the apex of the cone lies above the Earth's surface. The eclipse is annular at B C and partial at A B and C D.

to *aphelion* (the point most removed), the diameter of the Sun varies from 32' 30" to 31' 28". As for the apparent lunar diameter, its variation is somewhat more extended, namely 33' 30" to 29' 21", between the passage from apogee to perigee of our satellite. The limits of the apparent size of the Moon enclose therefore those of the Sun and this explains the varied appearance of the eclipses of the Sun.

An eclipse of the Sun cannot be *total* unless the apparent diameter of the Moon is at least as great as that of the Sun. If it is smaller the eclipse is *annular*, that is to say that at the moment when the centres of the two discs are coincident the edges of the Sun still remain visible in the form of a ring. These two types of eclipse are only observable in predetermined places ; in the neighbourhood of these special points the eclipse is of necessity *partial* (Figs. 34 and 35).

Sometimes a fourth type of eclipse is mentioned which lies between the total and the annular. It is called *a beaded eclipse*, because the shining crown which surrounds the lunar disc is discontinuous and it resembles somewhat a necklace of pearls. This phenomenon is due to the fact that the contour of the Moon is far from being perfectly smooth ; when the solar diameter is only slightly greater than the lunar diameter the roughness due to the mountains of our satellite is sufficiently great to break the continuity of the very narrow crown in numerous places. The shining pearls which are then formed have been given the name of *Baily's Beads*. These can also be seen when there is a total eclipse ; they appear at the moment when the eclipse is about to become complete, at the edge of the lunar disc which leaves the last portion of the Sun still visible. In this case the phenomenon only lasts a few seconds ; for the same reason it can reappear immediately after the end of the eclipse.

Fig. 35. — The 3 types of eclipse of the Sun. When the lunar trajectory is such that the centres of the Sun and Moon coincide appreciably, the eclipse is total if the apparent lunar diameter is greater than that of the Sun; if it is smaller, then the eclipse is annular. The magnitude of the partial eclipse shown in the diagram (middle right) is about 0.42 which means that 42 % of the solar diameter is hidden behind the Moon. It is obvious that this does not mean that 42 % of the Sun's surface is obscured.

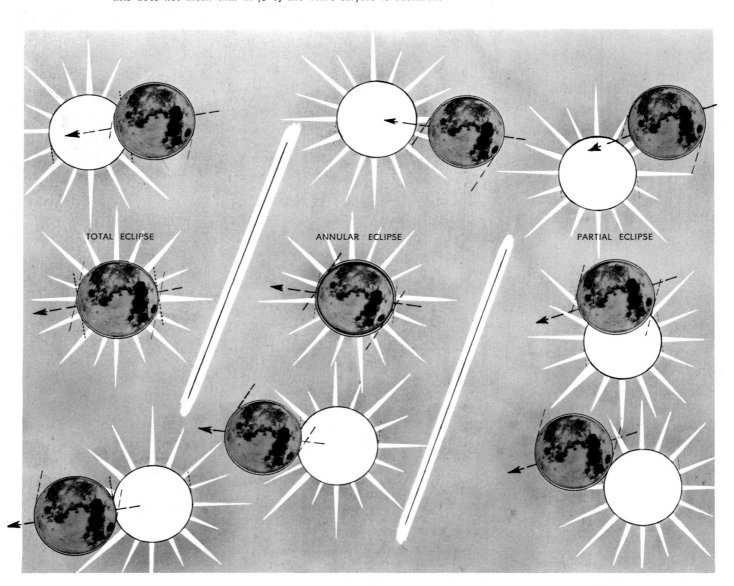

TOTAL ECLIPSE   ANNULAR ECLIPSE   PARTIAL ECLIPSE

Total eclipse of the Sun 15 February 1961. — *Photos 16-17.* — *The very different exposure times used for these photographs (1/8 sec for photo 16 and 7 sec for 17) show clearly solar eruptions in the first case and the extent of the solar corona in the second.*
(*Photos taken at Laigueglia, Italy, between 7.34 a.m. and 7.35 a.m. U.T. by Joseph Ruland.*)

Shape and Motion of the Shadow

The calculation of the elements of a solar eclipse is much more complex than that of a lunar eclipse for it requires, amongst other supplementary operations, the determination of the *zone of visibility*. The dimensions of the shadow which forms on the surface of the Earth during a total eclipse are very variable : if the apparent diameters of the two bodies are absolutely equal, the point of the shadow cone just touches the Earth and the shadow is theoretically reduced to a simple point. If on the contrary the apparent diameters of the lunar and solar discs are respectively at a maximum and minimum, the shadow reaches its greatest dimensions ; it assumes then the form of an ellipse whose major axis measures 270 kilometres. The circular form is exceptional for the intersection of the shadow cone with the Earth is more frequently made in an oblique manner.

Throughout an eclipse the shadow moves over the surface of the Earth with a speed which is a function of two factors acting in opposite directions : the speed of the revolution of the Moon around the Earth and the speed of rotation of our sphere on its axis. The Moon moves in its orbit at almost a kilometre per second and this gives the shadow area a speed of translation towards the east approaching 3400 kilometres per hour. If the rotation of the Earth caused the point touched by the shadow to move towards the east with the same speed, then the dark zone would not move, but this other motion is appreciably slower, and it depends besides on the latitude of the point under consideration. Being zero at the poles it reaches its maximum value at the equator, namely 1670 kilometres per hour. Whatever may be the cause, therefore, the shadow always moves towards the east. As its velocity is equal to the speed of the shadow area diminished by that conferred on the eclipsed region by the rotation of the Earth, the nearer the Sun's shadow passes to the equator, the less is this velocity.

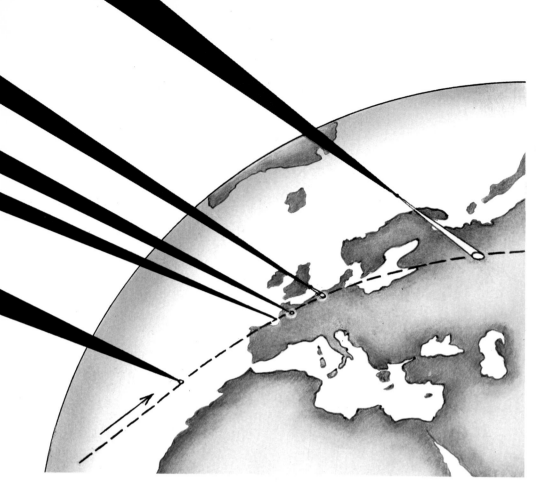

Fig. 36. — The eclipse of 17 April 1912. *This eclipse, total in the Atlantic, became annular almost at the very moment the shadow cone reached the continent of Europe.*

Fig. 37. — The eclipse of 15 February 1961. *This eclipse began at 7.30 a.m., 230 km to the south-west of Brest. The zone of totality crossed the south of France, the north of Italy, Yugoslavia, northern Bulgaria, southern Rumania and finally the U.S.S.R. from the Crimea to northern Siberia. The maximum duration of the total phase was 2 min 45 sec near Rostov. As for the width of the path of totality, it varied between 194 and 250 km. These relatively large values were because the Sun was low down in the sky, the shadow cast being therefore very elongated.*

The narrow band traced by the Sun's shadow on the Earth has been called the *zone* or *path of totality*. It is bordered on each side by a region where the eclipse is visible in its partial state and whose width can extend more than a thousand kilometres. Whilst the shadow cone sweeps the surface, the distance from the Moon to the different points touched on the Earth does not remain constant so that the eclipse does not necessarily keep the same character along all the path ; for example, it can be annular at the beginning, then become total and finally assume once more its annular appearance at the end (Figs. 36 and 37).

The maximum duration of a total eclipse of the Sun depends on three conditions. It goes without saying that the greater the apparent diameter of the Moon, the greater is the time of disappearance of the Sun. For this our satellite must be near its perigee and likewise the Sun must be at its greatest distance, that is to say the Earth must be at aphelion, which takes place about the 1st July. Finally, taking account of what has already been said on the variation of the speed of the shadow, the nearer the occurrence of the eclipse is to the equator, the longer it is. When these three conditions are fulfilled the duration of the eclipse reaches 7 minutes 58 seconds, but it is hardly necessary to add that this event is extremely rare. The last eclipses when the duration most closely approached this maximum value were those of the 8th July 1937 and the 20th June 1955 ; they slightly exceeded 7 minutes. Their paths of totality were both very close to the equator but, to the consternation of astronomers, they were practically confined to the oceans ; only Southern India and Siam were touched by the second eclipse. We will have to wait until the month of June in the year 2150 for the occurrence of an eclipse of 7 ¼ minutes.

One thing must be added here. If the positions of the Earth at aphelion and the Moon at perigee are such that the longest eclipse is possible, then they are also responsible for another consequence which tends on the contrary to reduce the duration of the eclipse. The Sun and the Moon do not make their way in the sky to meet each other ; both are moving in the same direction but at very different speeds so that correctly speaking there is not a crossing but a passing. Now the slower the body being passed and the quicker the body which is passing, the shorter the duration of such a manoeuvre and these conditions are precisely those of the case under consideration. In fact, according to Kepler's law, the Moon acquires its maximum speed at the moment it passes its perigee and the apparent motion of the Sun is slower when the Earth is at aphelion. It must therefore be concluded that the advantages resulting from the favourable positions occupied by the Earth and Moon are slightly attenuated by the unfavourable speeds to which these two bodies are subject when passing these points.

As the zone of visibility of a total eclipse is very narrow, a very long time naturally elapses, often several centuries, between the times when such a phenomenon takes place in one spot. Observers in Paris and Brussels who are now sixty or so can remember the last eclipse of this type which they were able to witness on the 17th April 1912. It will not be until the 11th August 1999 that this will take place again in the neighbourhood of Paris and after that it will be the 23rd September 2090 and the 4th June 2160.

Partial eclipses are of course a good deal more common and everyone has seen one in his lifetime. Usually these are total eclipses which appear partial to the observer, but sometimes they are of course truly partial. The latter are only seen in the regions surrounding a pole. In fact, if an eclipse is not total this is because the Earth does not enter the shadow cone although passing into the penumbra as with eclipses of the Moon. Now as the shadow cone always sweeps the space following a line which is practically perpendicular to the axis of rotation of the Earth, the only places it can approach without touching them are obviously the polar regions.

The Recurrence of Eclipses of the Sun

Eclipses of the Sun, like those of the Moon, are repeated according to rules which have been examined earlier on. Considered in their entirety, they constitute « families » in which each one is the repetition of the preceding, it being always understood that the reappearance takes place in a different region of the Earth. The change in the zone of visibility which is peculiar to the saros consists in a displacement in longitude as well as in latitude. The first can be explained by the fact that a saros comprises a whole number of days plus more or less a third. During this lapse of time the Earth performs the same whole number of rotations plus a third, so that the eclipse can now be seen in a country separated with respect to the first by 120° towards the west. If there were not simultaneously another displacement in latitude there would be three saros, that is every 54 years, for the eclipse to be visible in the same region.

The displacement in latitude is due to the obliquity of the lunar orbit and to the fact that the eclipse is possible as soon as the Sun is situated less than 18° 30' from a node. The first eclipse of a family takes place, therefore, when the Sun is at the extreme distance, whilst the second and following take place with Sun positions progressively closer to the node. If at the beginning of the cycle the Moon is at the north of the ecliptic, the first eclipses are only visible near the North Pole and they are, besides, partial, but the hidden portion of the solar disc is greater at each repetition of the phenomenon. At the end of a certain number of repetitions the eclipse becomes total but it is still only observable at a pole. At each return the path of totality undergoes a double displacement : it is displaced 120° towards the west and from 5 to 10° towards the south. This progress continues and whilst the path of totality approaches the equator the duration of the total phase increases until it reaches in this place its maximum value. The path then passes into the other hemisphere and continues to become displaced in the same way, but the duration of the total phase now diminishes. Finally, the last total eclipse of the family takes place at the South Pole ; it is followed by a certain number of partial eclipses progressively diminishing in magnitude until the moment when no more eclipse is possible. The Sun is now found at the other side of a node, 18° 30' away. It has been calculated that about 81 saros are necessary for a cycle of this type to be entirely completed. This represents about 1500 years. It is

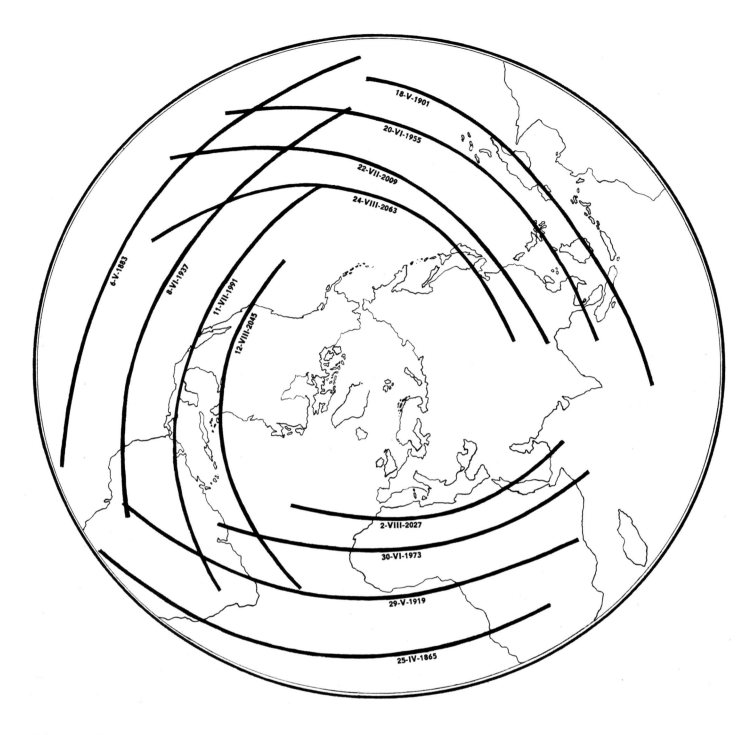

Fig. 38. — The family of eclipses in one saros. *The 12 eclipses whose paths of totality are shown above belong to one family, determined by the law of the saros. The displacement in latitude and longitude can be clearly seen.*

quite obvious that a family of eclipses can also begin at the South Pole. The way in which the paths of totality are now traced is the opposite in the case of the displacement in latitude (Fig. 38). It is equally clear that as the saros is not the only cycle concerning the return of eclipses, we can also group the latter following other modes of repetition and thus draw up other families. Taking, for example, as our basis a period of 939 synodic revolutions which corresponds to 1019 draconitic revolutions, we might be led to consider a family whose « life » would naturally be much longer but in which successive eclipses would be less displaced.

<h1 style="text-align:center">X</h1>

<h1 style="text-align:center">TIDES</h1>

The Moon, it is said, exercises an influence on the Earth in many respects. Many men are persuaded, for example, that the weather on Earth is governed by the phases of the Moon ; however, no scientist has ever supported this belief, at least in the way it is generally understood. On the other hand, a sufficiently brief argument can be made to render it worthless : the phases of the Moon are the same throughout the whole world ; now can it be reasonably conceived that at the moment when a phase changes the weather begins also to change simultaneously in all parts of the world ? Such an hypothesis is of course absurd ! There also exists the legend of the « April Moon » (1) which, despite the evidence given that it is in no way responsible for the harm attributed to it, nevertheless remains solidly anchored in the minds of a large number of farmers.

However, if we cannot deny *a priori* all the influences imputed to the Moon, there is one which no-one disputes, namely its effect on the tides. Today, in fact, everyone knows that as the Earth and the Moon are mutually attracted, the tides are the direct consequence of this action. There are, however, many who imagine that if the sea rises at a given place this is precisely because the Moon is passing at that moment above this particular spot. Now there are two tides a day whereas the Moon in its apparent motion only crosses the sky once every 24 hours ; in other words, whilst a tide takes place in a part of the Earth facing the Moon, another of equal importance is taking place in an antipodal region, that is to say on the side which is precisely the furthest away from our satellite. The problem is therefore more complicated than we think and in order to understand it, certain pecuiarities of the relative motions of the Earth and the Moon must be remembered.

The Mechanism of the Tides

It has been seen earlier (Fig. 8) that these two heavenly bodies revolve around their common centre of gravity ; consequently although the radius of the trajectory described by the centre of the Earth during each lunation is extremely small, it still remains true that this motion of revolution has an effect. Similarly, it has been stated concerning the behaviour of the satellite that a motion of revolution comprises two components, one of which acting tangentially to the real trajectory tends to make the satellite follow a straight line because of the inertia of the body, and the other acting towards the centre of rotation tends to pull in the satellite to this point as a consequence of the attraction which is exerted. This second component is none other than that which makes the satellite fall and it can be said that the fall is real and permanent, although at each moment compensated by the effects of the first component. For the same reason the Earth, like the Moon, is perpetually falling towards a particular point but this action is naturally extremely slight for our sphere.

Every falling body obeys the law of gravitation set forth by Newton. If it is solid its motion is identical with that which is imposed on its centre of gravity, but if it is fluid it is distorted during the fall. Newton's law stipulates in fact that the force of attraction is inversely proportional to the square of the distance over which it is exerted, so that if the object is voluminous the different particles which compose it are not attracted in an identical way. Those of the lower portion are attracted more strongly towards the Earth than the central point, which itself undergoes a greater attraction than the upper particles. If at departure the object is spherical, it becomes elongated in the vertical direction and adopts the form of an ellipsoid. In other words, the upper part moves away from the centre exactly like the lower part ; the latter is in some measure slightly ahead whilst the other is slightly behind. The magnitude of the separation from the centre does not depend on the absolute value of the force of attraction but only on the difference existing between the forces acting on the extreme points of the object (Fig. 39).

We can easily understand how the molecules of a fluid body act under the action of a field of forces by adopting a very simple experiment. By means of two pieces of elastic three balls are joined together on the

---

(1) (Translator's note.) During cloudless nights in Spring, plants may be affected by frost causing discoloration or « rusting ». The Moon receives the blame and is therefore called by French farmers « la lune rousse » (rust-coloured Moon).

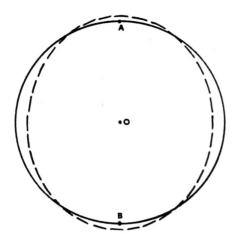

Fig. 39. — Distortion of a liquid falling body. *In its original state the body is considered to be spherical. Since point B is closest to the centre of the Earth, it undergoes the greatest attraction. Point 0 is somewhat less attracted and point A suffers the least attraction of all. If the body is free to fall, it becomes distorted since it is liquid and its shape is a function of the forces acting at different points. Consequently it assumes the shape of an ellipse.*

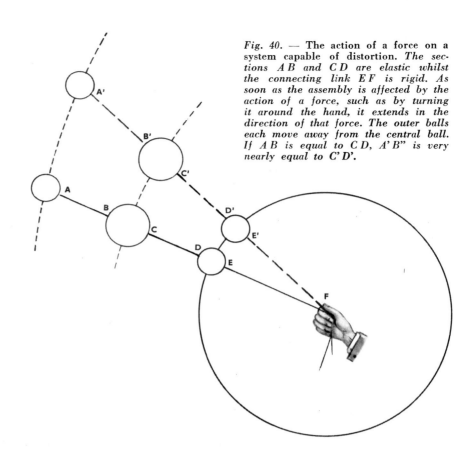

Fig. 40. — The action of a force on a system capable of distortion. *The sections A B and C D are elastic whilst the connecting link E F is rigid. As soon as the assembly is affected by the action of a force, such as by turning it around the hand, it extends in the direction of that force. The outer balls each move away from the central ball. If A B is equal to C D, A' B" is very nearly equal to C' D'.*

same straight line ; one of the outer balls in then joined by a string so as to continue the straight line. The other end of the string is held and the whole assembly is made to describe circles around the hand (Fig. 40). Under the action of centrifugal force the pieces of elastic lengthen and the outer balls both move further away from the one which lies between them. The molecules of a fluid body perform in a like manner under the influence of a force such as that of gravity ; the middle ball is similar to the central molecule and the two outer balls can be compared to the two molecules on opposite sides of the periphery.

The force which causes the Earth to « fall » affects the seas in the same way as gravity influences a fluid object. In order to follow the argument more easily, let us suppose that the terrestrial sphere is entirely covered with water, then two bulges would normally be formed ; the sea consequently rises both on the side facing the Moon and on the opposite side. Since these two « high tides » can only be produced by causing a simultaneous lowering of the waters in the two intermediate regions, there must of necessity be low tides in these areas. Finally, given that the tide follows the Moon in its motion around the Earth and that our satellite takes 24 hours 50 minutes to do a complete circle, there is a tide every 12 hours 25 minutes.

Spring and Neap Tides

The Moon is not the only celestial body which attracts the Earth ; the Sun exerts a similar action and at first sight it would seem that the latter should be greater. This is not so, however, firstly because of the considerably greater distance which separates us from the Sun and secondly from the fact that it is not the absolute value

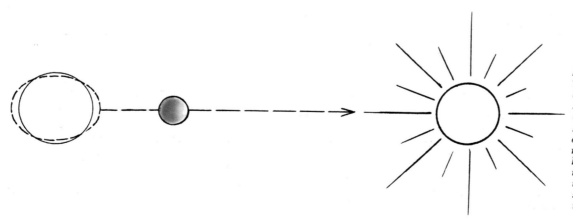

Fig. 41. — Spring tides. *The Sun and the Moon, being in line on the same side of the Earth (obviously at new Moon), their action is additive and the tide reaches its maximum height. The same result is achieved when the two bodies are in opposition, namely at the time of full Moon.*

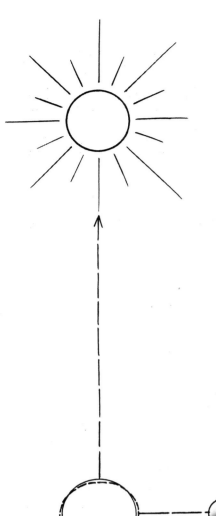

Fig. 42. — Neap tides. *The Sun and the Moon are here acting at right angles to each other. If the action of each was equal there would be no tide at this time, but since the lunar attraction is 2.2 times that of the Sun, a relatively small tide nevertheless occurs.*

of the attractive force which is concerned but the differential effect on the extreme points. In fact, the attraction of the Moon is 2.2 times stronger than that of the Sun.

Since the two bodies are constantly acting together the resultant effect varies between large limits depending on their respective positions in the sky. When the Sun and the Moon are in the same direction or even in directions diametrically opposed, their effects add together. The tides at syzygy are consequently considerably greater and are called *spring tides* (Fig. 41). On the other hand when the Sun and the Moon are in quadrature they act against each other and the effect is at a minimum ; at these times the *neap tides* occur (Fig. 42).

The height of the tides depends also on other factors ; for instance the angle made between the orbital planes of the Sun and the Moon and the plane of the equator enters into the calculation. The closer the two bodies approach the latter plane the more powerful is their action on the oceans. Now at the equinoxes the trajectory of the Sun is situated in the plane of the equator and that of the Moon is only a little way off ; *equinoctial tides* benefit, therefore, from a rather stronger force. Likewise, since the distance which separates us from the Moon has to be reckoned with, the tides are greater when our satellite is at perigee than when it is at apogee.

Theoretical and Actual Tides

The elementary theory which has just been expressed supposes that the Earth is completely submerged by the oceans. As the geographical situation of the Earth is quite different, the problem which exists in reality is not one only of astronomy but also of hydrodynamics. That is why the effects produced by tides in different parts of the world are often peculiar and sometimes even in direct contradiction with the conclusions which ought seemingly to be drawn.

Since by its apparent motion the Moon crosses the sky from east to west and circles the Earth in 24 hours 50 minutes, the bulge which it brings about is required to move over the surface of the Earth in the same direction and at the same speed. But the tidal wave thus created must make its way through all sorts of passages, broad, narrow, shallow and deep, which are consequences of the tortuous configuration of the coastline and which constitute a great number of obstacles opposing its regular propagation. The rotation of the Earth in which all the liquid mass of the globe is involved, the friction of water on the seabeds and its viscosity are equal causes of slowing down. Besides, the static theory which takes no account of the forces of inertia and which supposes an instantaneous state of equilibrium of the liquid surface under the action of the attracting force, is only just acceptable for the situation in the middle of the oceans.

To tell the truth, the force of attraction which is exerted on the seas is extremely weak ; calculation shows that the lunar action can scarcely give rise to a change of level of more than 54 centimetres whilst the solar action produces only 25 at most, so that at times of spring tides the total difference in level should not exceed 79 centimetres... This is rather strange and will be examined further on for this figure is not even reached in the centre of the ocean ; in Honolulu, for example, the maximum tide is 50 centimetres and does not exceed 60 centimetres on the islands of Réunion and St. Helena.

The situation is entirely different near the coast. As the driven surge of the tidal wave is impeded, currents which can sometimes be violent are created, the direction of which can be diametrically opposed to that of normal propagation ; amongst others, this is so in the Channel where the tide extends the whole length from west to east. A first consequence of the secondary motions is the lag which exists between the moment when the Moon transits the meridian at a predetermined spot and that when the tide is high at this same place. When the phenomenon occurs in a very confined sea, this lag is obviously all the more pronounced. At Brest for example the lag is 3 hours 45 minutes and it increases progressively for the ports situated more and more deeply in the narrow passage formed by the Channel. It reaches 12 hours 15 minutes at Dunkirk so that there then occurs a double anomaly ; on the one hand, the tidal wave arrives clearly from the west and on the other hand, although the tide is high at the very moment of the transit of the Moon, the correlation which seems obvious between these two events does not in fact exist. If the tide is high it is because our satellite has passed by half a day earlier above the antipodal point. The interval which elapses between the theoretical and the real time of high tide has been given the name of *the port establishment*, also known as the *mean high water interval*. As we have just seen, this element varies considerably from one port to another but it is constant for a given place.

The second consequence which results from the perturbations created by coasts is also quite spectacular : the tidal currents pouring into certain narrow seas cause variations in the level along the coastline which have no connection at all with those predicted by static theory. Here again the more irregular the configuration of the land masses and the more unequal the depths, then the more accentuated the effect ; in seas containing a large number of shoals, such as in the centre of bays or straits, the active pressure developed by the wave can cause the water to rise to enormous heights. The coasts of the Channel are in this respect quite characteristic. The average difference in level between low and high tide is approximately 4 metres off the peninsula of Brittany but it reaches 10 metres at Mont St. Michel ; on the contrary, at Cherbourg it is again no more than 4 metres. The equinoctial tides are sometimes extraordinary : at Granville, for example, it may reach 15 metres. France however does not hold the records for the highest tides ; Canada in the Bay of Fundy has tides of approximately 20 metres in height. In Argentina at Port Gallegos the maximum is 18 metres, and in Great Britain in the Bristol Channel tides reaching 16 metres have been measured.

It goes without saying that the tides represent a formidable energy which men have always tried to harness. Attempts to utilise this power have been made in numerous places but especially where the change in level has been most considerable ; unfortunately, difficulties of a technical nature have continually held up the realisation of these projects. Today, however, they seem to have been entirely overcome since a power station to utilise tidal energy is in construction in France in the estuary of the Rance ; the available power provided by the sea in this place has been estimated at 20 million kilowatts ! Canada also is considering the construction of a similar power plant, a fact which will obviously surprise no-one since this country will in this manner be able to take advantage of the immense oceanic resources which nature has given it.

In the estuary of great rivers the tide sometimes produces quite violent phenomena. At the moment when the sea rises the water rushes into the river mouth and if the depth is slight, the rising wave has to struggle not only against the out-flowing current of the river but also against the resistive force of friction. As a result there is a piling up of water which ultimately overcomes the obstacles and makes its way up the river course, producing quite high waves. This phenomenon is well-known in a number of estuaries — on the Trent it is called the *eagre*, and on the Seine the *mascaret* where near Quillebœuf the change in level can be as much as 3 metres.

If in certain seas the tide undergoes tremendous variations in its level, in others, on the contrary, it can scarcely be noticed. In a general way this is the case of seas which are for the most part landlocked such as the Mediterranean and the Adriatic. The height of the tide at a maximum at the far end of the latter does not exceed 85 centimetres, and in Marseilles it attains at the very most 20 centimetres. The Red Sea and the Caribbean are in a similar situation.

Finally, the capricious nature of the currents is sometimes such that they create absolutely paradoxical situations. At Southampton four high tides occur each day as the rising water comes up to the Solent and then Spithead, whereas at Do Son, on the coasts of Tonkin, there is only one tide a day. In Tahiti there is only one tide and, even more remarkable, this unique one always takes place at the same time. Such exceptional cases can only be explained by very localised considerations and very complex mathematics.

Earth Tides

It has been said earlier on that according to theoretical calculation the change in level caused by spring tides ought to reach 79 centimetres and that in fact in the middle of the oceans it does not exceed 50 to 60 centimetres ; in these places, then, there is an anomaly opposite to that which takes place near the coast, and it was Kelvin (1824-1907) who discovered the explanation of this phenomenon. Contrary to the belief engendered by the expression « the rigid Earth », the Earth's crust has in no way an absolute stability ; in the same way as the oceans, it undergoes the effects of lunar and solar attraction and although distinctly slight in amount, it is the object of deformation which occurs with the same rhythm as the tides. In other words, the tidal wave does not only affect the waters of the oceans but likewise the crust of the Earth ; two daily bulges diametrically opposed make their way round our sphere, very slightly lifting the ground. The result of this is that in the centre of the oceans where the water very closely obeys the laws of the static theory of tides, a measurement made from the sea bed cannot give the real value of the deformation suffered by the hydrosphere, that is to say by the liquid sphere, since the base of this itself is raised up. In fact, the change in level of the sea as measured only represents about two-thirds of the theoretical value, the third part relating entirely to the deformation of the crust, that is to say to the *Earth tide*.

Several instruments have been devised to measure the Earth tides, amongst which mention must first be made of the *gravimeter*. This apparatus is simply a balance of extreme sensitivity, the function of which is to measure variations of gravity. If these were known, the corresponding variations in height could be deduced by an application of Newton's law. It is quite obvious that since the gravimeter must be able to reveal changes in level of the order of a metre, that is to say variations in gravity which are extraordinarily slight, it must of course contain an amplifier ; modern gravimeters comprise high fidelity electronic amplifiers possessing a high degree of amplification.

Another type of apparatus has been conceived to measure the vertical deviations following upon the Earth tides. If it was impossible to distort the crust, a plumbline, that is a vertical pendulum, suspended free from any disturbance, would remain indefinitely above the same point on the ground. But as this crust undulates as a consequence of the periodical passage of the two bulges, this point is also periodically displaced and in proportion to the force of the tide. Here again it is a question of imperceptible displacements some hundredth of a micron for a plumbline a metre in length. Theory tells us, however, that the deviations of a rigid vertical

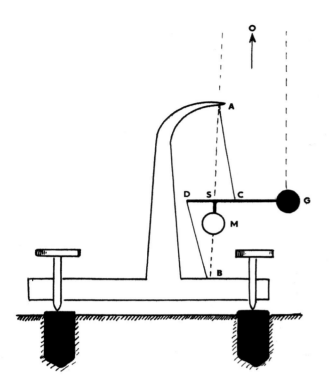

pendulum can be considerably amplified if the axis of rotation, normally horizontal, is made vertical. Bringing this axis almost to the vertical position, which is the same as saying that the oscillating element is practically horizontal, the apparatus called the *horizontal pendulum* is formed. This possesses the very interesting property of being the equivalent of a very much longer vertical pendulum and in theory at any rate can be as long as desired (Fig. 43).

A horizontal pendulum placed on the ground faithfully records the variations in inclination of the ground in relation to the vertical. These fluctuations appear in the form of a curve of sinusoidal appearance, comprising in 24 hours two maxima and two minima, exactly like the curves of oceanic tides. The amplitude of the sine wave varies itself according to the rhythm of the lunation ; it reaches its greatest value at syzygy, a fact which needs no further explanation since at this moment the lunar and solar actions are additive (Fig. 44).

Fig. 43. — Diagram of a horizontal pendulum. The horizontal pendulum S G is suspended by two wires fixed at the two points D and C. The points of attachment of these wires to the bracket at A and B form an imaginary straight line which is practically vertical and this is the axis of rotation of the pendulum. It can be shown that S G is the equivalent of a vertical pendulum of length G O, the virtual point of suspension O being at the junction of the imaginary axis A B and the perpendicular line produced at G on the horizontal pendulum. Since these two straight lines are almost parallel, point O is some considerable distance away.
The mirror M, rigidly fixed to the pendulum, receives a ray of light from a fixed source and reflects it on to a revolving drum ; the slightest movement is thus amplified and photographically recorded.

The O R B horizontal pendulum. — *Photo 18. — The O R B horizontal pendulum constructed at the Royal Observatory of Belgium and perfected by the astronomers J. Verbaandert and P. Melchior consists primarily of a horizontal beam very freely suspended from a rigid support by two fine wires. The support, beam and suspension wires are made of fused silica (SiO₂), a substance which, together with other remarkable properties, possesses a coefficient of thermal expansion of almost zero. The fine silica wires have great tensile strength and yet are very flexible; their resistance to torsion is very slight.*
If the geometric axis of rotation is made almost vertical, gravity has a considerably reduced effect on its equilibrium. The slightest external force, such as the tide — producing force of the Sun and Moon, is capable of making the moving arm deviate from its state of equilibrium since, by producing minute variations in the tilt of rocky ground on which the apparatus rests, it upsets the equilibrium of the latter and the moving arm begins to oscillate. A small mirror fixed to the pendulum causes the oscillations to be recorded by photographic means; the mirror reflects a narrow beam of light which then produces an image on sensitized paper transported at about 5.5 millimetres per hour.
Numerous examples of the O R B pendulum now exist throughout the world.

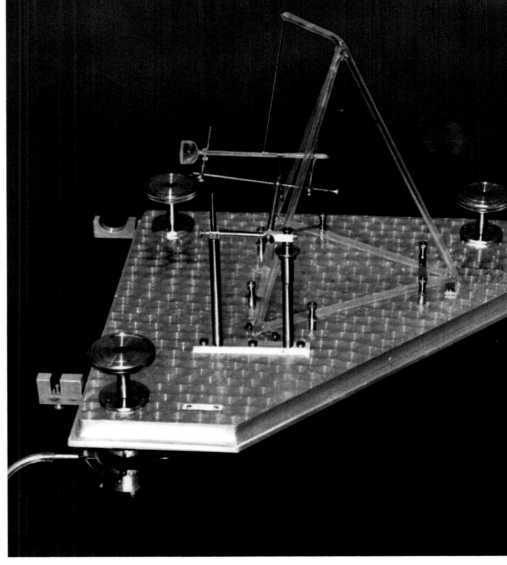

Fig. 44. — Recordings of a terrestrial tide.
This diagram shows the result of a photographic recording made at the Sclaigneaux research station (Namur province in Belgium) in an old mining gallery some 80 metres below the surface of the Earth. The microvariations in the inclination of the ground, which in the first place cause the recorded motion of the pendulum, have a maximum amplitude corresponding to an inclination in the

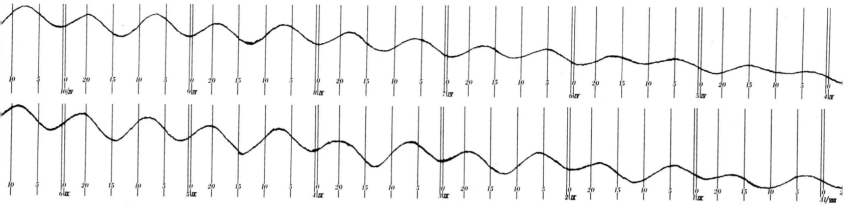

east-west direction of ± 0".02. The minimum amplitude corresponds to a variation in the inclination of ± 0".008. The graph shows clearly the twice daily tide; the amplitude of the variation is greatest at the moment of syzygy and minimum at quadrature.

The weak oscillations of random nature which break up the saw-tooth formation of the curve indicate the microvibrations of the ground or minute seismic tremors permanently agitating the Earth's crust; these originate principally in the beating of the ocean waves on the coast. The shocks thus produced on the land masses cause a tremor which is propagated for thousands of kilometres inside the Earth.

The whole graph is inclined slightly towards the right and this spurious effect is generally described by geophysicists as drift. It is as if the periodic tide is superimposed on a slow movement of the ground following a secular pattern. In reality, the causes of this effect, which are annoying when precise measurements are required, are largely instrumental. The minute movements of the ground have in fact such a small amplitude that the distortion factor of even the most stable and rigid substances used in the construction of measuring instruments must be taken into account. It is, however, probable that in a number of regions on the Earth slow tectonic movements are superimposed on the purely instrumental causes, all contributing to the drift.

Atmospheric Tides

Since the lunar attraction is capable of distorting the crust of the Earth, it also makes itself felt on the molecules of air which form our atmosphere. In fact, these *atmospheric tides* do exist and are governed by the same cyclic laws as ordinary tides, the importance of which is consequently greatest at the moments of syzygy. In fact, they can cause the barometric pressure to vary although within extremely small limits ; nevertheless those who believe in the influence of the Moon on the weather make a particular point of this to support their thesis. Is this argument really worth consideration ? Before going any further it is important to say that the lunar attraction has a periodic character, the rhythm of which is relatively rapid : 12 hours after its appearance in a given region it is already having an influence 180 degrees away. Since the changes which affect the weather are on the contrary generally slow, there can be no question of seeing the slightest correlation between the two categories of variations. In fact, we could only accept the reality of the lunar influence on the weather at the times of full and new Moon, that is to say when the atmospheric tides are strongest. Now even in these cases the variations in barometric pressure are minute and the preceding objection concerning the very fugitive action of the tides is still quite valid. In reality, the meteorological variations are due to causes of quite another nature, as complex as they are profound, which far exceed in importance those which could be created by atmospheric tides. At the very most it would be correct to admit that the latter are capable of playing a very weak role in specific cases.

XI

DESCRIPTION
OF LUNAR RELIEF

The Sun apart, and perhaps also Venus which certain people can see as a crescent, our satellite is the only celestial body which appears to the naked eye other than as a simple shining point of light. Moreover, its apparent dimensions are sufficient to allow us roughly to distinguish several types of lunar regions or at least spots of different hues. Certain people endowed with good sight can even discern actual contours or see the outline of one or other characteristic figure such as the feminine profile of the « Lady in the Moon ».
Seen through binoculars these figures are perfectly clear and bright regions stand out distinctly from dark parts. At certain periods of the lunation when the illumination is favourable it is even possible to make out some undulation of the surface or other salient features. But it is obvious that it is only in the telescope that the lunar surface can be seen in all its wondrous glory and the countless details can be examined. On looking at a photograph of the Moon taken in a telescope the most striking feature is the extraordinary appearance of

Particularly devastated areas of the Moon. — *Photos 19 and 20. — The areas of the Moon shown in these photographs resemble to a remarkable degree a bombarded battlefield.*

31 May 1944 — age : 9.57 days.   (*Photos : Pic du Midi Observatory.*)   *15 January 1944 — age : 19.05 days.*

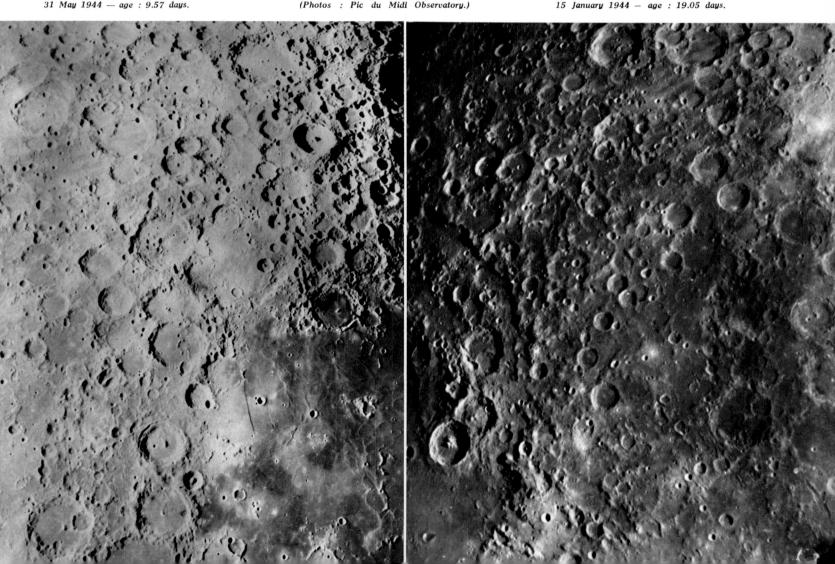

devastation ; the surface is literally riddled with holes of every dimension, such as a battlefield after a violent bombardment. But equally striking is the difference in appearance upon examination of the photographs of the same region taken at various moments of the lunation : a particular undulation which on one seems to reveal a deep cavity scarcely appears on the other as a slight depression. Such contrasts are entirely due to the conditions of illumination from one moment to the next.

The Importance of Illumination

In order to make a reasonable study of the lunar relief, a moment must be chosen when the illumination accentuates this, that is to say when it causes long shadows ; consequently it is necessary to choose a time when the region to be observed is near the terminator. In this zone in fact the Sun's rays come from the horizon and shadows are projected some distance. For example, the central part of the Moon can be examined best when it is at one of the quarters and not, as might be believed, when it is full. In this latter case the light of the Sun shines down from the zenith, the shadows are practically non-existent and the lunar surface seems exceptionally flat. However, this does not mean that the observation of the full Moon is without interest ; it reveals details of another type, which themselves bring an important contribution to the study of the configuration of our satellite. In fact, it is thanks to the continual variation in illumination that astronomers

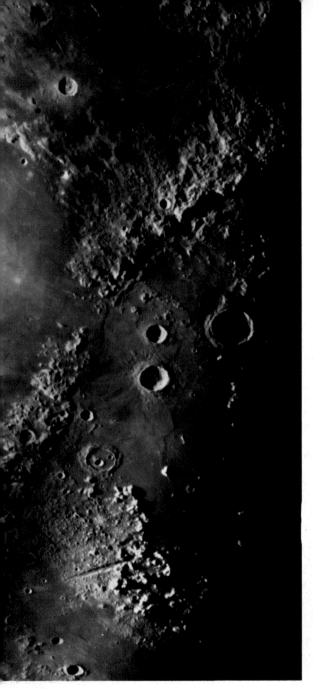

Oblique illumination. — *Photo 21.* — *The lunar formations which lie quite close to the terminator receive an oblique illumination and their shadows are consequently very long. The Caucasus mountains (lower middle) are here a striking example of this.*

(Photo : Pic du Midi Observatory, 3 January 1944 — age : 7.53 days.)

Opposite illumination. — *Photos 22 and 23.* — *These two photographs covering approximately the same region show the latter under illumination from diametrically opposed points. Certain formations have therefore quite different appearances. Note in particular the Straight Wall (upper middle) which appears black on photo 22 and white in 23.*

(Photos : Pic du Midi Observatory.) 31 March 1944 — age : 9.57 days. 17 January 1944 — age : 21.6 days.

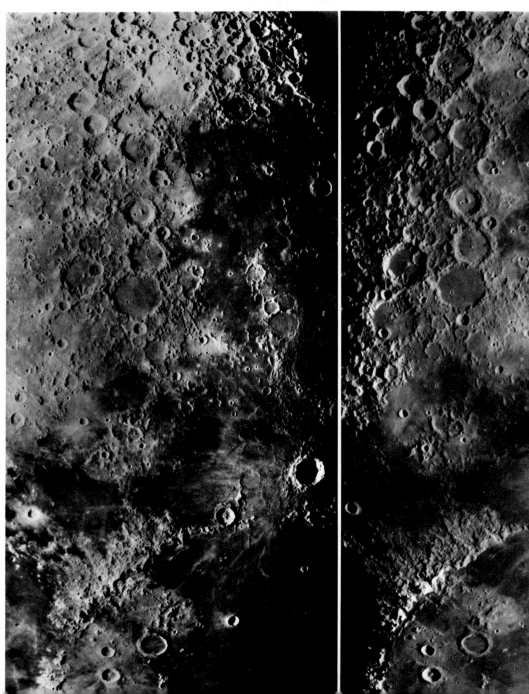

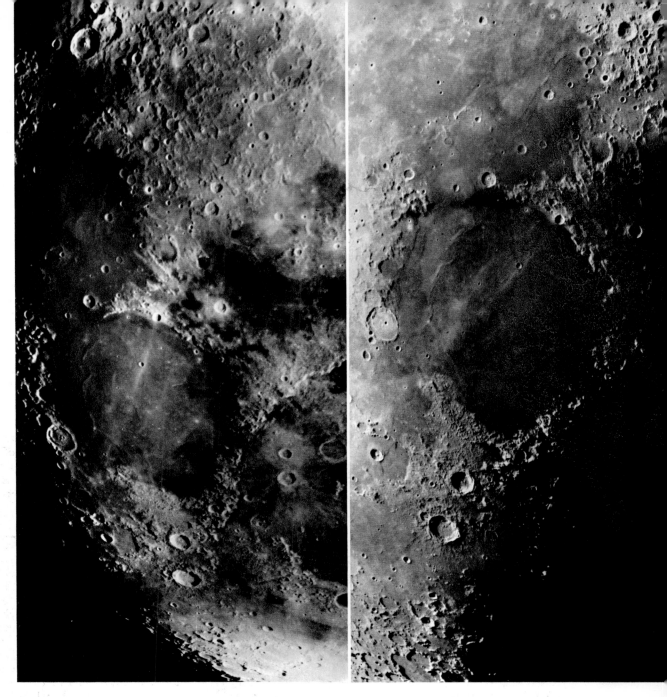

can not only detect the nature of lunar formations but also calculate the dimensions of them with great accuracy. When the terrestrial atmosphere is calm and clear the telescope can pick out orographic (mountainous) features scarcely more than a kilometre in length ; with more powerful instruments, with a magnification approaching 1000, isolated areas can be distinguished whose diameters do not exceed 200 metres, and areas less than 400 to 500 metres apart can be separated. Dark straight line markings can also be spotted having a width of only 100 metres or so, craters no more than 600 metres across can be identified. When the illumination skims the surface, differences in level of a few tens of metres can be determined thanks to the extremely elongated shadows which are projected at this time.

* * *

Present on the lunar surface is a considerable number of different topographic formations ; the three most characteristic are the *seas*, the *ring formations* and the *mountains*.

The Seas

The term « sea » is obviously incorrect, since it refers to something quite different from a sea on Earth, but we know with what respect astronomers maintain, either voluntarily or by force of circumstance, the nomenclature of ancient times. In this respect we have only to think of the constellations of stars, whose mythological names were given to them some 2000 years ago. As for the names given to the various lunar formations and in particular to the seas, they are some centuries old, dating from a period when astronomers observed the Moon for the first time with a telescope and thought it similar to the Earth. As this period was especially imbued with lyricism and imagination, it has left as a legacy to us a series of quite fantastic expressions : Sea of Serenity, Ocean of Storms, Sea of Nectar, Bay of Dew, Lake of Dreams, Marsh of Decay, etc. Although we know today that all these seas do not contain a drop of water, nevertheless it must be recognized that confusion was easy for

Three great lunar formations. — *Photo 26.* — *This photograph shows clearly the variety of lunar formations and particularly the respective appearance of maria (seas), mountains and craters.*

(Photo : Pic du Midi Observatory.)
1 May 1944 — age : 8.95 days.

observers possessing quite rudimentary instruments. In fact those areas where the colour is distinctly darker than other formations constitute zones of relatively smooth terrain. For the most part they possess an approximately circular shape, and there are many amongst them that like the craters are surrounded by a mountain rampart. From their centre there sometimes fan out radial *striae* or *rills*, huge crevasses in the ground. In certain cases *ridges* cover their surface ; these are folds exhibiting slight differences in level — a few hundred metres at the most — and which cannot be seen except when lit very obliquely. Therefore they cannot be discovered except when near the terminator and for this same reason only those which are parallel to this line of separation can be seen. Their appearance is very complex ; usually they all lie in the same direction but there are some which cross each other. On the whole they are situated towards the edges of the sea and skirt the « coastline ». The American astronomer G. P. Kuiper has disclosed slight fissures and even types of extrusion on the ridge of certain folds.

The Ring Formations

The huge amphitheatres which for a long time have been usually known as *craters* because of their alleged resemblance to the mouths of volcanoes, make up the most characteristic, the most varied and also the most numerous formations of the Moon. The smallest discernible in the telescope have a diameter of the order of a kilometre, and there is every good reason to believe that there must be many more of smaller dimensions. The greatest, on the other hand, can sometimes reach nearly 250 kilometres across. The total number of ring formations is estimated at some 20,000 to 30,000. About 600 of these formations have been given a name generally borrowed from the names of philosophers, scientists and astronomers of all ages.

The craters vary amongst themselves as much in appearance as in dimension. Some are very deep whilst others are scarcely so or seem to have been filled with matter sometimes to such an extent that they almost disappear beneath a layer similar to dust. The interiors are sometimes flat and even — some have been discovered which shine at the time of full Moon — and yet from others a relatively high peak or mountain massif rises up. The sides or ramparts differ from one type of crater to another : the ridges are sometimes rounded, sometimes steep and craggy, particularities which give undeniable proof in the determination of the age of the formation.

Such a variety of structure has prompted certain astronomers to establish a methodical classification of the craters and use is sometimes made of a

The crater Wargentin. — *Photo 27.* — *Wargentin is the model for a crater in which the liquid matter had originally a volume greater than the depression. The lava must have poured over into the neighbouring crater.*

Photo : Pic du Midi Observatory.)
27 November 1955 at 9.02 p.m.

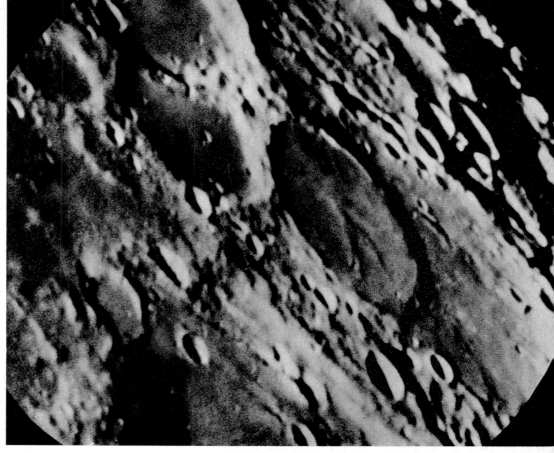

Clavius. — *Photo 28.* — *This crater is one of the largest on the Moon considered by many selenographers as the model for the walled plain.*

(Photo : Mount Wilson & Palomar Observatories — 200-inch telescope.)

(Photo : Paris Observatory.)

(Photo Observatories Mount Wilson and Palomar.)

terminology conceived by the English selenographer Neison at the end of the last century. To tell the truth, the proposed names have a character rather more descriptive than representative of a category in relation to the origin of a formation. With this system the following can be distinguished ; *walled plains* which are gigantic formations having the appearance of enormous circular arenas surrounded by a massive rampart ; *mountain rings* similar to the former but smaller in diameter ; *ringed plains* in which the walls, still very high, are linked to the arena by a slope frequently divided into terraces ; *crater plains* differing little from the preceding type but somewhat smaller ; *craterlets* ; *crater cones* which resemble small volcanoes, and *crater-pits*, simple wall-less openings.

Certain craters are surrounded by a *ray system* similar to the halo used by artists in the adornment of the heads of saints ; in other words a bright ring from which numerous straight shafts of equally bright colour radiate. This cannot be seen when the terminator is in the immediate neighbourhood and its brilliance is simply a function of the angle of illumination ; it is maximum when the illumination is intense. The most remarkable ray systems are those of the craters Copernicus and Tycho ; the hundreds of rays which seem to escape from the latter are astonishingly long and one of them extends over more than half the lunar disc. At full Moon they appear in marvellous fashion. Since they throw no shade they cannot be considered as some form of undulation, particularly since they span every obstacle ; they are in fact marks on the ground.

Ray system : Tycho. — *Photos 29 and 30.* — *These two photographs, taken respectively a little before and a little after full Moon, show quite remarkably the ray system surrounding the well-known crater Tycho.*

The Mountains

The lunar mountains have a very different appearance to ours ; although they may have craggy ridges they are not particularly steep, but they are very high and proportionally even higher than terrestrial mountains if we take into account the respective masses of the two spheres. The highest summits, those which are situated in the Leibnitz mountains, exceed 8000 metres, that is to say that they almost reach the height of Mount Everest. It must be stated, however, that these heights have been calculated with respect to the surrounding ground since on the Moon there is no common reference level. Whilst on Earth an altitude may be defined by saying that it is so much above « sea level », such a statement is impossible for the Moon. Consequently, this renders any comparison useless and would only be valid if we could imagine our two hemispheres drained of their oceans. Now since there are abysses at the bottom of the sea with depths reaching thousands of metres, it would be discovered in the end that the extreme variations in height are indeed more considerable on Earth than on the Moon (Fig. 45).

Whilst a large part of the lunar mountains are grouped together and form mountain chains analogous to those on Earth, others on the contrary are completely isolated in the plain ; the mountains Pico and Piton are typical examples of this. Certain precipitous formations are

Ray system : Copernicus. — *Photo 31.* — *The ray system of Copernicus, a young crater, is remarkable. The rays extend in every conceivable direction.*

(Photo : Mount Wilson & Palomar — 100-inch telescope.)

68

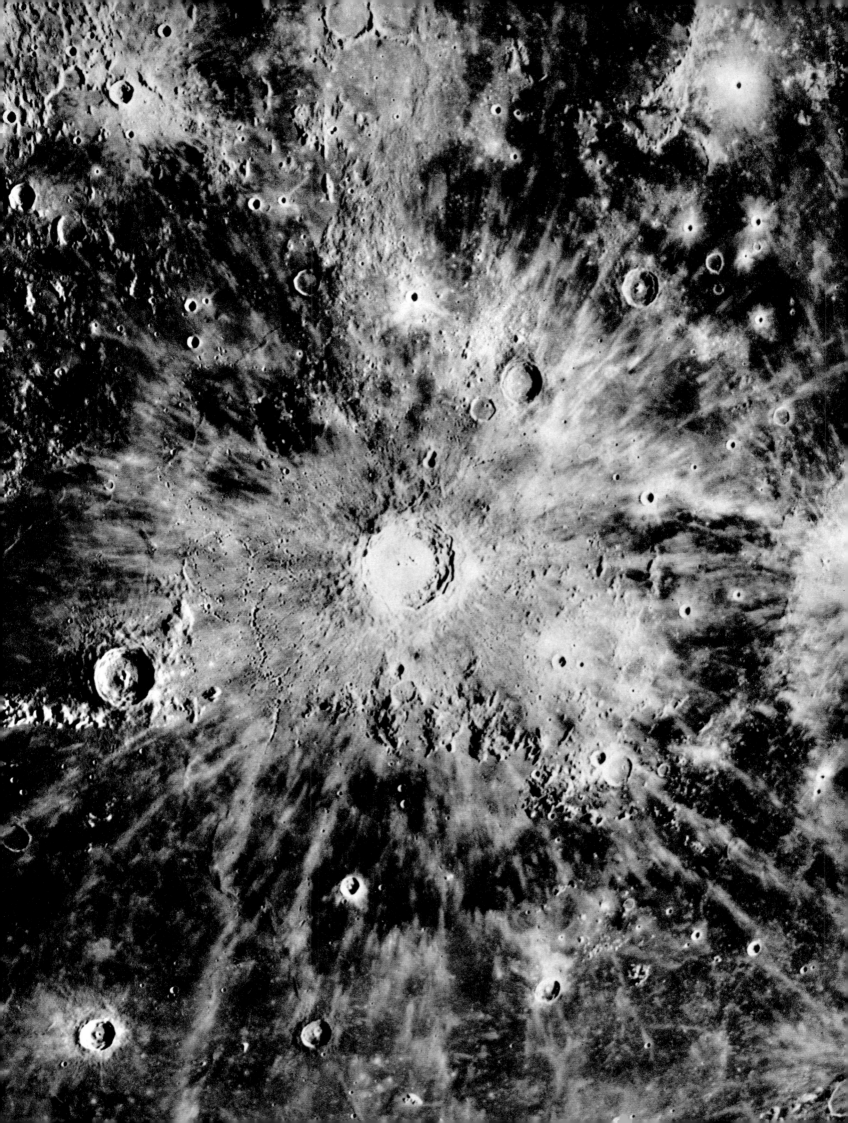

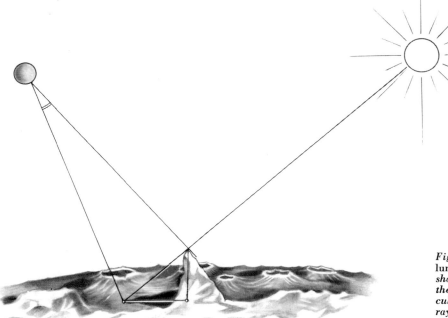

Fig. 45. — The measurement of the height of lunar mountains. *The length of the projected shadow can be measured from the Earth. Since the phase of the Moon is known when the calculation is made, the angle at which the Sun's rays strike may be deduced. The calculation is simply therefore a trigonometrical problem.*

equally characteristic : the Straight Wall, for example, which is a gigantic fault having the appearance of a cliff 1000 kilometres long and some 300 metres high.

The names which have been given to the mountains and chains on the Moon are in some cases the repetition of those which describe ours ; thus we find Mont Blanc, the Apennines, the Caucasus, the Alps. Other names call to mind scientists and mathematicians.

Amongst the lunar mountains may also be classified small hills which take on the appearance of extinct volcanoes. These are hillocks with diameters of about 8 kilometres, slopes of 1 in 20, and having craters at the top about 800 metres across. These formations which often occur in groups abound especially in the seas. As they have the same colour as the latter they cannot be observed during full Moon.

The Clefts

To conclude this description of the various lunar formations mention must be made of the clefts. These are crevasses or fissures in the ground, the length of which can reach hundreds of kilometres, the width a few kilometres and the depth several hundreds of metres. About 200 of them are known, the greatest number being discovered quite recently, and they have been placed in two categories : *broken clefts* and *regular clefts*. The first have the appearance of broken lines, the sections of which are at an acute angle to each other. In general they are shallow but relatively wide, and their appearance shows that they have been progressively filled. The shapes described by these crevasses are particularly noteworthy : often their departure point is a small crater and the various lengths appear like lines joining neighbouring craterlets more or less in the same direction. Some clefts of this type can be discovered in the interior of some of the great craters such as Gassendi, for example.

Regular clefts, as their name indicates, are long faults having the appearance of straight lines or arcs of circles of very great radius. Their width and depth are appreciably constant. They are found almost exclusively in the neighbourhood of the boundaries separating the land masses from the seas ; they are parallel to the edge and sometimes grouped in two or three parallel lines such as those on the west side of the Mare Humorum.

The Lady in the Moon. — *Photo 32.* — *The profile of the lady can be clearly seen in binoculars and even sometimes with the naked eye at full Moon.*

XII

COMPOSITION
OF THE LUNAR SURFACE

A telescopic examination of the lunar surface cannot give any useful indication of the nature of the substances which compose it. In compensation, the analysis of radiations which reach us, whether in the form of heat, light or radio waves, is in this respect capable of providing extremely precise information.

The Moon does not shine by its own light ; the light it receives is natural since this emanates directly from a light source and in this case from the Sun itself. On the contrary the light it sends to us is more or less altered, as is all light which meets an obstacle and which therefore is subject to the effects of well-known optical phenomena : absorption, reflection, refraction, polarization. Since physicists have established how bodies of different substances react under light and how they modify it, they can therefore, by analyzing the light so altered through encountering a body of unknown nature, determine the composition of the surface quite accurately. This method of investigation is practically the only one which can be applied to the study of very remote bodies.

Analysis of Lunar Light

The light from the Moon has always been the object of innumerable measurements ; those which were used to determine the value of the lunar albedo were amongst the most delicate. It is known today that the maximum amount of light dispensed by the Moon — that which it sends to us when it is full — is almost half a million times less intense than that which reaches us from the Sun. The amount of light coming from the Moon obviously increases at the same time as the phase of the Moon but the proportion in which this increase operates is not immediately apparent. One is tempted to believe, for example, that the full Moon is twice as luminous as at one of the quarters. Nothing is further from the truth : it is in fact twelve or thirteen times more, and the reason lies in the angle of incidence of the Sun's rays. When the illumination is oblique — and this is the case with an important fraction of the lunar surface at first or last quarter — then the shadows thrown by the mountains and other undulations are very long ; therefore they reduce considerably the portion of the disc which acts as a mirror. Moreover the first quarter reflects rather more light than the last, the two halves of the lunar disc not possessing similar areas of dark zones. One further interesting detail, full Moons in winter are slightly more luminous than those in summer since they are higher in the sky and the rays of light which come from them fall less obliquely on Earth.

Photometric and Colorimetric Measurements

The unevenness of the lunar surface can be determined quite accurately by the *photometric study* of different regions. The latter shine at a maximum when the incident light rays are at right angles to the surface, that is to say, at full Moon, but the way in which the light varies with the phase is the same for every region whether bright or dark, whether « seas », land masses, mountain walls, crater floors or ray systems. This proves that the ground is composed of the same material at every point. The Dutch astronomer J. van Diggelen has calculated the value of shadows existing in cavities and clefts of different shapes and differently illuminated ; he arrived at the conclusion that at least two-thirds of the lunar surface must be composed of ellipsoidal cavities usually more deep than wide. Comparing the results of his lunar observations with those which he had obtained in the laboratory from naturally occurring and artificial samples of rock, he was able to conclude that the lunar material is very rough and that it is riddled with numerous irregular cavities of every dimension lying close to each other. Highly aerated vesicular slag corresponds closely to this definition. *Colorimetric analysis* has also given several clues to the chemical nature of bodies. The method used is also essentially comparative ; it therefore likewise implies measurements in the laboratory on numerous examples. The results obtained so far are not conclusive ; none of the substances examined, limestone, granite, basalt, sandstone, or gneiss, had reproduced exactly the properties of the lunar surface. One fact has however been determined : the colour of the

71

ground is very appreciably uniform as has been shown by recent measurements of colour indices particularly of the ray systems taken in Soviet observatories ; the values obtained are remarkably constant. The Russian astronomer N.N. Sytinskaya thinks that the colour of the lunar material is due to the effects produced by the collision of small meteorites. The heat released at the moment of impact is capable of decomposing the silicates into oxides of iron, the colours of which are particularly dark.

Measurements of Polarization

However, amongst all the methods of studying the lunar surface based on the examination of the light emanating from our satellite the greatest advance that has been made by astronomers is in the study of *polarization*. Natural light can be physically broken down into two independent waves of specific frequency and equal intensity, vibrating in directions perpendicular to the direction of propagation. When a beam of natural light strikes a body, it is reduced in strength owing to a certain absorption by the latter. Moreover the fraction which is not absorbed and which is therefore rediffused no longer shows the same characteristics as the incident light ; the two waves no longer have the same intensity, the amplitude of one is reduced whilst that of the other preserves its original value. This can be expressed by saying that the light is polarized and the plane of the unaffected wave gives its name to the direction of polarization.

The light which comes to us from the Moon is only partially polarized for it still contains a certain amount of natural light ; but the proportion of affected light as well as the direction of polarization are precious clues essentially linked to the nature of the lunar surface. The determination of these elements is one of the most delicate of operations, for the measurements must consider all regions of the Moon and must be made successively under every condition of illumination occurring throughout a lunation. Provided these precautions are taken the results can be validly compared to those arising from measurements made in a laboratory on samples of substances which are presumed to be similar to those being identified.

From 1924 to 1926 the French astronomer Bernard Lyot undertook measurements of polarization of the light reflected by the Moon on a large scale. In addition he initiated a large number of laboratory analyses and was thus able to conclude that the lunar surface must be composed of a powdery material bearing a strong resemblance to volcanic ash. This research deserves great admiration not only because of the high degree of accuracy with which the measurements were made, but also because the results can be attributed to the quality of the instruments which Lyot personally perfected or which he himself invented.

The researches on polarized light were continued by the French astronomer Audouin Dollfus, an old colleague of Lyot, who set out, amongst other studies, to determine the polarization of those surfaces of the Moon showing a marked declivity. Since there is a critical angle for every slope beyond which a powder must of necessity slide off and thus lay bare the underlying rock, it would be right to suppose that the steep parts of the Moon are not covered with the same material as the flat surfaces. Now this is not so ; experiments which have been made on the cliff forming the Straight Wall and on the slopes of a valley, have shown that there is no difference in polarization between sloping regions and the neighbouring areas. Dollfus was therefore able to conclude that this powder not only adheres to the surface, but that it fills the wrinkled cavities under the action of forces which appear greater than gravity.

Depolarization

Audouin Dollfus continued his investigations still further by measuring the polarization of the Earthshine. The aim of this new experiment can be explained as follows. The Earthshine is caused by the reflection of light from the « full Earth » on that portion of the lunar disc which is not directly lit by the Sun. Since these rays of light have passed through our atmosphere they are considerably polarized. Now any substance illuminated by a source of light already polarized possesses the property of restoring a part of the absorbed waves ; this phenomenon is called *depolarization*. Besides, the proportion restored depends on the nature of the substance, so that this coefficient of depolarization as well as the coefficient of polarization provides a parameter capable of contributing to the desired identification.

Besides, the examination of the Earthshine presents a two-fold interest. Not only does it allow the texture of the lunar surface to be discovered, but it also provides very interesting information concerning the polarization of the light from Earth. In fact, the polarization of the Earthshine is none other than that of the Earth seen from space, corrected by the amount of depolarization. In order to check this correction Dollfus made several ascents in a free balloon taking with him a polarimeter. In this way he was able to measure at great height the polarization of the light coming from the Earth.

Lyot's conclusions were in this way confirmed and improved : the lunar surface is very probably covered with a substance composed of granules of volcanic ash, irregular, opaque and of small dimensions. The overlying layer is very likely powdery, perhaps very shallow, but covering the surface everywhere.

In the radiation spectrum which nowadays is a continuous scale on which science classifies by wavelength or frequency all the vibrations that are known, light only occupies an extremely narrow band. It is contiguous with the band forming the region of infra-red rays or thermal radiations. Moreover there is no gap between the two neighbouring parts, showing that the properties of such vibrations do not change sharply from one category to another ; on the contrary, they vary imperceptibly and so the nature of light waves having a wavelength corresponding to dark red is very near that of thermal radiation (Fig. 46).

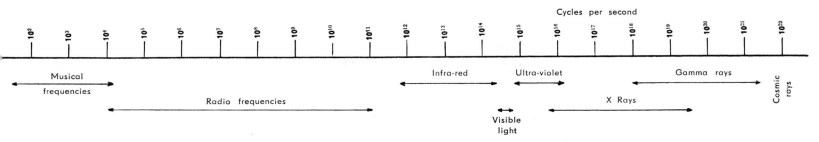

Fig. 46. — Table of frequencies. *In the frequency spectrum light waves only occupy a very small segment; from 375 billion (10^{12}) cycles per second at extreme red to 770 billion cycles per second at extreme violet.*

Analysis of the Lunar Temperature

Just like any body that receives heat, the Moon radiates a certain quantity in return ; this radiation, which can be detected like that of light, provides astronomers with very useful information particularly concerning the *depth* of the lunar surface.

Generally speaking, bodies do not transmit different types of radiation equally. Just as they may be transparent or opaque to light, so they show varying degrees of transparency or opacity towards other radiation and notably towards heat rays. The power of penetration is directly proportional to the wavelength of the radiation, and it is this property which has been put to great profit by astronomers. By analyzing the radiations at different wavelengths they can to a certain extent build up a picture of the texture of the ground at different depths.

The first measurements of the temperature of the Moon were carried out by Lord Rosse 75 years ago, by means of a thermocouple. His results were rather inaccurate apart from the value of the maximum temperature which was appreciably the same as that which is considered correct today. Much more recently, the American astronomers E. Pettit and S.B. Nicholson used the same method of measurement, using, however, a much more accurate thermocouple which they fitted to the 100-inch telescope on Mount Wilson. The aperture of this instrument was at the time the greatest in the world so that they captured the maximum possible thermal energy. In this way they were able to establish that the Moon is bombarded by thermal radiation having a wavelength extending from 8 to 14 microns with a maximum intensity at 10 microns (10 thousandths of a millimetre). That portion of the lunar disc which receives the Sun's rays vertically reaches a temperature very slightly above 100° whilst the temperature of the dark part plunges down to —150° C. Finally, and this is important, the variation of the temperature follows the variation of sunlight without any appreciable lag. In other words, when the Sun rises on the Moon the temperature of the ground rises sharply, and as soon as it sets the temperature falls immediately. A confirmation of this phenomenon was found by the two observers during different eclipses of the Moon : at the moment of the obscuration of the Moon the temperature falls with the same rapidity and rises quite quickly at the end of the eclipse.

Since the lunar surface is only very slightly affected by the variations in temperature, the material which covers it is consequently a bad conductor of heat. By referring to the laws of heat propagation, Pettit and Nicholson attempted to determine its nature and thickness ; they suggested that it was formed of a very fine powder, the granules of which did not measure more than a tenth of a millimetre ; and moreover the thickness of the layer would be several millimetres.

On wavelengths above those of infra-red extending some considerable way in the spectrum, no more thermal emission from the Moon is detected, but on wavelengths between 1 and 1.6 millimeters is found again. During the eclipse of the Moon on the 18 th January 1954, the American astrophysicist W. Sinton was able to detect a radiation having a wavelength of 1.5 millimetres. He deduced the corresponding temperatures which were 30° as the initial temperature and — 100° as the minimum temperature. He also stated that the variations of solar illumination were followed by the variations in temperature but with a delay of 35 minutes.

Further deductions resulted from these experiments : the smaller values, whether of the maximum temperature or of the amplitude of the thermal variation, together with the lag which affects the variation in the lunar temperature, show that the origin of the radiation on 1.5 millimetres is situated in a relatively deep layer less under the influence of the Sun. After carrying out comparative measurements on various materials Sinton concluded that the characteristics of the superficial layer must be those of powdered basalt, having a nature somewhere between that of pumice and a meteorite.

Further interesting observations have been made quite recently in this respect. During the eclipse of the Moon on the 13th March 1960 astronomers of the Dominion Observatory noticed that the craters of Tycho, Copernicus and Aristarchus did not cool as much as the surrounding regions ; the temperature of Tycho remained 40° to 60° higher than the others. Sinton confirmed this phenomenon during the eclipse of the Moon on the 5th December 1960 : Tycho held its temperature round about — 35° during all the phase of totality. The explanation could be the following : Tycho's superficial layer of powder could be thinner than that of the surrounding zone, possibly only 0.3 millimetre.

The Analysis of Radio Emissions

A third category of radiation coming from the Moon and observed for some years now has also brought a serious contribution to the study of the lunar surface. These are emissions, belonging to the band beyond the infra-red region of the radiation spectrum. The analysis of these phenomena stems from the new science of radio astronomy whose aim is the reception and interpretation of the different types of radio emission generated by cosmic radio sources. Radio astronomical techniques are very specialized as the radio waves cannot be perceived by our senses as with light waves, whose wavelengths are directly linked to colours, and as in the case of thermal waves. In order to detect a radio emission it is necessary to employ receivers capable of being tuned to receive a large bandwidth, often requiring patient and painstaking research.

Investigations that followed the reception of the first radio emissions from the Moon confirmed the law concerning the penetration by radiation : the greater the wavelength, the deeper the penetration. In 1949 the Australian astronomers J.H. Piddington and H.C. Minnet detected a lunar emission on a wavelength of 1.25 centimetres. Indubitably it was coming from layers deeper than those which cause the millimetre waves. The measurements taken showed, moreover, that the variations in temperature followed the variations in illumination with a delay of almost 4 days ; further, the amplitude of the thermal variation was 2.5 times weaker than that which had been shown in the emission on 10 microns. Still more recently, research has been carried out on wavelengths of 8 millimetres and 33 centimetres, but the conclusions have not yet been clearly established. In fact, up to the moment they have not brought any new conclusive evidence on the thickness of the deposit of powder which covers the lunar surface or on the nature of the material itself. However, there is no doubt that in the near future when radio astronomy has perfected its methods of investigation important information will be found by this means.

Analysis of Radar Echoes

Radar is a further research procedure based on the analysis of radiations. The technique employed does not depend on emissions that permanently bombard our satellite, but rather on the echoes of radio signals specially transmitted for this purpose by a station on Earth and beamed towards the Moon. Radar, in fact, not only allows us to determine the distance separating the Moon from the Earth, but also provides by the analysis of the echoes certain clues concerning the nature of the reflecting surface. The scale on which these measurements is made is much greater than that which is used for photometric analysis ; since polarisation measurements give us information on the composition of the lunar material on a smaller scale than that of photometry, the three methods are therefore mutually complementary.

The Moon behaves towards radio waves in the same way as a mirror to light rays. If the mirror is absolutely flat and perfectly polished, the amount of light that it reflects in a given direction is a maximum ; but if it is made up of a number of facets lying approximatively side by side in the same plane and if further some of these are imperfectly polished, the light reflected in the direction under consideration is appreciably attenuated. Finally, if the mirror is spherical the quantity of light reflected is even further reduced since the reflection takes place in all directions and the dispersion is considerable. In particular, if the observer lies in the direction of the source he can only receive the light ray reflected by that part of the surface perpendicular to this direction.

When a radio signal is sent towards the Moon, one can expect to receive principally the echoes emanating from the central part of the lunar disc, that is to say, from a small cap whose surface can be considered as perpendicular to the direction of the incident ray. Since 1949, the year of the transmission of the first radar signal towards the Moon, several experiments have been carried out on various wavelengths. They have shown that the echo effectively comprises two parts : the first coming from the central region of the Moon and constituting approximately 80 per cent of the reflected energy, whilst the second is due to irregularities of the lunar surface and comes from the whole of the visible disc.

It has been possible to estimate the dimensions of the reflecting cap thanks to the studies which have been made on the distortion present in the echo. Jodrell Bank situated in Cheshire in the north of England has established that 50 per cent of the energy is reflected within the first 50 μ s (millionths of second) following the start of the echo. As electromagnetic waves are propagated at a speed of 300,000 kilometres a second, the distance traversed in these 50 μ s is 15 kilometres ; but since the radar signals make their journey in both directions the distance in the direction of the incident ray between the surface elements causing the beginning and the end of the echo is 7.5 kilometres. From this it may be concluded that the spherical cap situated at the centre of the lunar disc and reflecting the major part of the signals must have a diameter of about 340 kilometres.

This method of analysis using radar techniques is too recent for any definitive and accurate general conclusions to be drawn. Nevertheless, the interpretation of results already obtained and notably of those concerning the echoes coming from the central cap show that to the nearest kilometre the lunar surface is relatively smooth ; its slopes, slight and rounded, are not greater than 1 in 10.

XIII

THE ORIGIN
OF LUNAR FORMATIONS

Few problems have given rise to so much discussion and hypothesis in the scientific world as that of the alleged origin of the lunar formations. Even today, although the field of discussion is considerably restricted, several theories persist, each one having its defenders. The first to examine the question quite naturally tried to explain the evolution of the lunar surface by comparing it with the crust of the Earth ; that is to say, they were normally led to attribute the innumerable features to internal forces, particularly in the case of the ring formations which litter the surface of our satellite. From this conception various theories have arisen that are called volcanic or plutonic. However other scientists were subsequently inclined to believe in the intervention of external forces and imputed the origin of the ring formations to the collision of the Moon with celestial material of various dimensions. This theory, called meteoric, had practically no supporters at the beginning for it raised numerous objections to which its few defenders found it then impossible to reply in a satisfying manner.

Volcanic Theories

One of the first plutonic hypotheses was formulated in 1874 by Nasmyth and Carpenter. According to these two English astronomers, each crater was born from the eruption of a volcano which has poured out its lava around it in the manner of a spring spouting from the ground. The peripheral wall is said to have been formed in the first place from matter thrown some considerable way out, when the eruption was at its height. Terraces would then have been formed during the following phase, a period corresponding to a diminution of the expulsive force ; in certain cases a central peak would have been thrown up as a result of a final ejection of lava of considerably less power. In exceptional cases, however, this final flow would have completely filled the arena with lava, an hypothesis which would explain the nature of certain formations such as the crater of Wargentin.

Although at first sight very attractive, the theory of Nasmyth and Carpenter will not stand a detailed examination ; besides, it does not rest on the authority of any valid comparison between the alleged volcanoes of the Moon and those which are found on Earth. The latter are mountains, by definition being raised up above the general surface, having the shape of a cone and a summit displaying a proportionally very narrow mouth. The lunar crater on the contrary is a depression, having a considerable aperture. Another decisive argument is that when matter, whatever it may be, is poured onto the ground, it forms a pile, the slope of which varies according to its content (stones, gravel, earth, sand). Now this natural angle is never attained in the circular wall of a lunar crater. Furthermore, how can it be admitted that the ejections of lava can have taken place so uniformly in every direction, especially in the case of craters having a diameter of 200 kilometres ? Finally, this theory does not explain why the central peak never reaches the level of the circular ramparts.

At the end of the last century, the French astronomers Loewy and Puiseux put forward another plutonic hypothesis, which for the most part revised theories already formulated about 1665 by the English physicist R. Hooke, a contemporary of Newton. As a consequence of the slight gravity and density of our satellite, the strength of the internal forces would have been sufficient to raise up the lunar crust at a time when the Moon was still in a paste-like state. Blisters or swellings would have been formed and would have burst just like bubbles do on the surface of custard which is brought to the boil. As they collapsed they would have given birth to the craters ; then, since the forces of expansion were still capable of further effort, they would have pierced an opening at a weak point, that is to say at the centre of the crater. The lava would then have escaped by this point thus building up a central peak.

Various physicists have proposed modifications to the theories of Loewy and Puiseux and particularly it has been suggested that the ejection of the lava could have been caused by a splitting of the lunar shell at the moment of its solidification. Chimneys would have been created in the cracks at the most exposed places through which the still fluid internal magma would have poured towards the outside and would thus have brought about a series of domes of various dimensions. At the time of cooling, the continuous action of the gases would have caused the collapse of these domes, thus causing the appearance of the craters. This hypothesis explains the alignment of the craters along cleft lines which certain selenographers refuse to attribute to simple chance.

The Arizona crater. — *Photo 33.* — *The diameter of this cavity of meteoric origin is 1,200 metres and its depth 180 metres.*   (Photo Arizona Highways.)

The Meteoric Theory

It would seem that we must consider the German astronomer Gruithuisen who lived from 1774 to 1852 as the originator of the meteoric theory. At the end of the 19th Century the English physicist Proctor likewise defended this hypothesis but without success. Why, it was principally objected, if our satellite had been really bombarded, was it that Earth had not received its share of the projectiles, the dimensions and number of which in proportion should be quite colossal considering the greater surface area ? Now the traces left on Earth by the fall of meteorites are extremely rare and their extent bear no comparison with that of lunar craters. Why, it was added, are the craters practically all of circular form, whereas evidence would seem to show if there had in fact been a collision with heavenly bodies that they would have more often fallen obliquely than vertically ? The majority of the craters thus scooped out should all in consequence be elongated.

Such is the strange outcome of events that the last two world wars have brought back the ideas of Gruithuisen and Proctor into favour. In fact, one cannot deny the similarity between the lunar surface and a landscape ravaged by the poundings of artillery, by aerial bombardment and the explosion of subterranean mines. Studying the problem again, the defenders of the meteoric theory began by replying to the first objection. If the Earth does not show the same devastations as the Moon it is mainly because it is surrounded by an atmosphere ; daily there fall towards the Earth tons of meteorites, but since they penetrate the layers of air with great velocity they heat up to such an extent that they burst into flame and melt almost instantaneously. These are the incandescent bodies which we often see in the night and which we usually call quite incorrectly shooting stars. Sometimes it happens, although very exceptionally, that certain of these celestial bodies reach the ground unburnt ; they then produce enormous cavities such as the celebrated Arizona crater in America.

To this destruction of meteorites by the atmosphere must be added another phenomenon of great importance which itself explains the rarity of traces of meteoric impact on our sphere : namely, the erosion which takes place ceaselessly. In fact, this weathering is infinitely more intense on the surface of the Earth than on the Moon, for the principal agent is water, an unknown element on our satellite. To tell the truth, when considered on the scale of geological time the elimination of terrestrial meteoric craters by erosion takes place almost immediately after their formation.

With similar reasoning one can reply to the following often expressed observation : « If each lunar crater is, in fact, the result of a meteoric impact, we ought to witness a similar cataclysm in our time ; the examination which would then be made of the phenomenon would bring everybody into agreement. » Unfortunately this agreement which is correct in itself has very little chance of being tested. In fact, it is estimated that a meteorite of great dimension falls on Earth once every 200 years. Given that the Moon has a surface area 13.5 times smaller, logically it ought to receive such a one every 2700 years ; and since its visible surface represents 60 per cent of the total area, mankind is not normally called on to be present at the birth of a new lunar crater except approximately once every 4500 years ! This figure which will discourage the most patient observers nevertheless requires confirmation by several complementary proofs. There is one of particular interest. Today, more than 20,000 craters are known, which, at the frequency which has just been indicated, would have required some hundred million years. There is nothing here which should cause surprise as soon as one takes into account the presumed age of the Moon (4 ½ thousand million years), but over and above this it implies a new hypothesis : all the craters formed before this time should have indeed disappeared. Now how can we reasonably admit this further supposition if our satellite does not undergo any effects of erosion ? The destructive agencies known on Earth do not exist on the Moon ; deprived of water and atmosphere, it knows neither wind, rain nor running water, all the factors which have contributed to give our mountains their rounded and contoured outlines. Does this virtually mean that phenomena of another type would not have been capable of modifying the appearance of its surface ?

Lunar Erosion

Certain scientists have suggested that the variations of temperature, the frequency of which is indeed relatively rapid, were such as to bring about a disintegration of the rocky surface followed by a slow crumbling. Others have considered the effects of ultra-violet and X-rays, which could destroy the links of certain crystalline lattices. In order to examine these hypotheses, Dollfus calculated the forces involved within the lunar rocks occurring at the sudden cooling observed at sunset and during eclipses. According to his conclusions the thermal variations are incapable of causing a systematic crumbling and do not therefore explain the powdery nature of the lunar soil.

However, amongst the characteristic elements of our satellite there are some particularly useful in providing a clue to the process of formation and displacement of the lunar dust; these are the ray systems. Only the recent ring formations possess them, which proves the rapidity and facility with which they become obliterated. Their structure determined quite accurately by photometric and polarimetric analyses is identical with that of the surrounding material, indicating a simple change of state of a similar substance. They can be considered, therefore, as the deposits of powder coming from the debris ejected in a circle following the explosion responsible for the crater. As the thickness of the powdery layer is probably smaller than the depth of the hollows ceaselessly produced by small meteorites, it is supposed that this intermittent bombardment moves the soil sufficiently to cause the progressive disappearance of the rays. Viewed in more general terms, this surface disintegration following upon the continued repeated meteoric impacts probably constitutes the principal cause of lunar erosion. Sytinskaya, who has compared the probable quantity of micrometeorites

The age of craters. — Photo 34. — Two craters of very different ages lie side by side in this photograph. On the right the great crater Copernicus, a young formation with jagged ridges surrounded by a ray system. In the middle of the photo, and of the same height, Stadius, a very old formation disappearing almost entirely under the dust.

(Photo : Mount Wilson & Palomar Observatories — 200-inch telescope.)

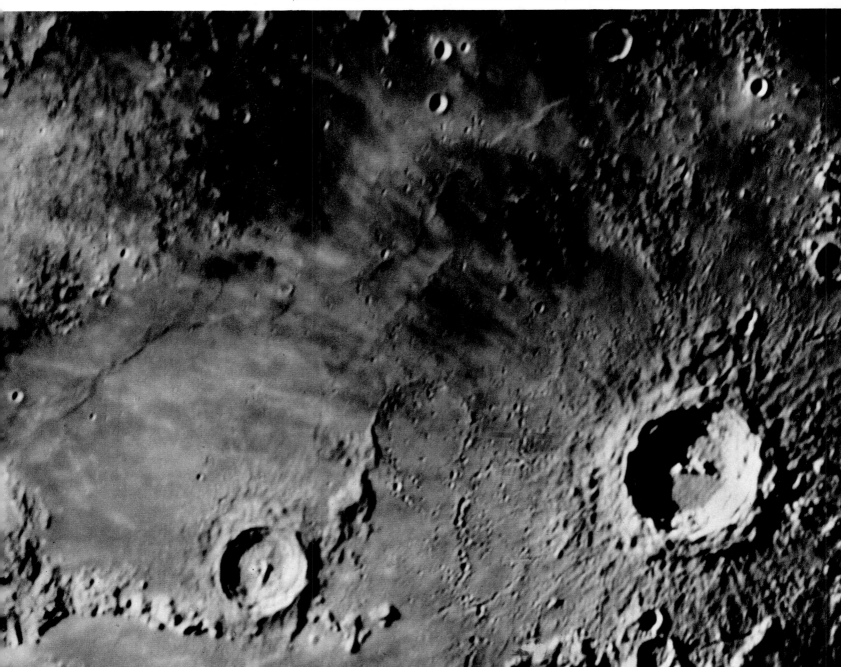

Central peaks. — *Photo 35. — On this photograph which represents a central region of the Moon it is easy to distinguish the craters which possess a peak or a central mountain region. Note also the considerable number of clefts which cover the region and which are nearly all in a north-south direction.*

(Photo : Pic du Midi Observatory — age : 8.55 days.)

reaching the lunar surface with cosmic dust counted by artificial satellites confirms this conclusion.

The special nature of lunar erosion has given astronomers the possibility of determining approximately the age of various formations on our satellite. The very oldest rings such as Clavius do not show any sharp arête and on their edges, faintly marked, are often superimposed other craters formed later on ; they never possess a ray system. Indeed, the oldest such as Stadius only appear for the most part buried beneath dust or filled with new material ; often no more than a vague outline can be distinguished. Young craters are characterized on the contrary by tapering walls, sharp arêtes, and frequently by the presence of a ray system. In many cases, they visibly encroach on old formations.

A Defence of the Meteoric Theory

If the lunar craters can clearly be differentiated from each other according to their age and their dimensions, their proportions are nevertheless governed by a common rule. Sappers and artillery men know perfectly well the constant ratio linking the diameter and the depth of a shell hole, whatever may be the absolute dimensions of these elements. The American scientist R.B.Baldwin set out to verify the universality of this relationship by investigating the widest possible range of craters ; he noted the characteristics of all the shell holes caused by the impact of a projectile or alleged projectile, from the smallest — those of light bombs or mines — to the most immense, that is to say lunar ring formations. His conclusions have been categorical : there is effectively a continuity in the law of the variation in diameter as a function of the depth.

However, amongst the numerous problems which the meteoric theory ought to explain, the thorniest was without doubt the enormous difference which exists between the dimensions of lunar ring formations and those of the rare terrestrial craters having the same origin. It must be remembered, in fact, that the Arizona crater placed on the Moon would scarcely form a craterlet.

Several physicists have studied the mechanism of falling meteorites, notably Gifford, Baldwin, Opic

The Mare Imbrium (Sea of Rains). — *Photo 36.*
(Photo : Mount Wilson & Palomar Observatories — 100-inch telescope.)

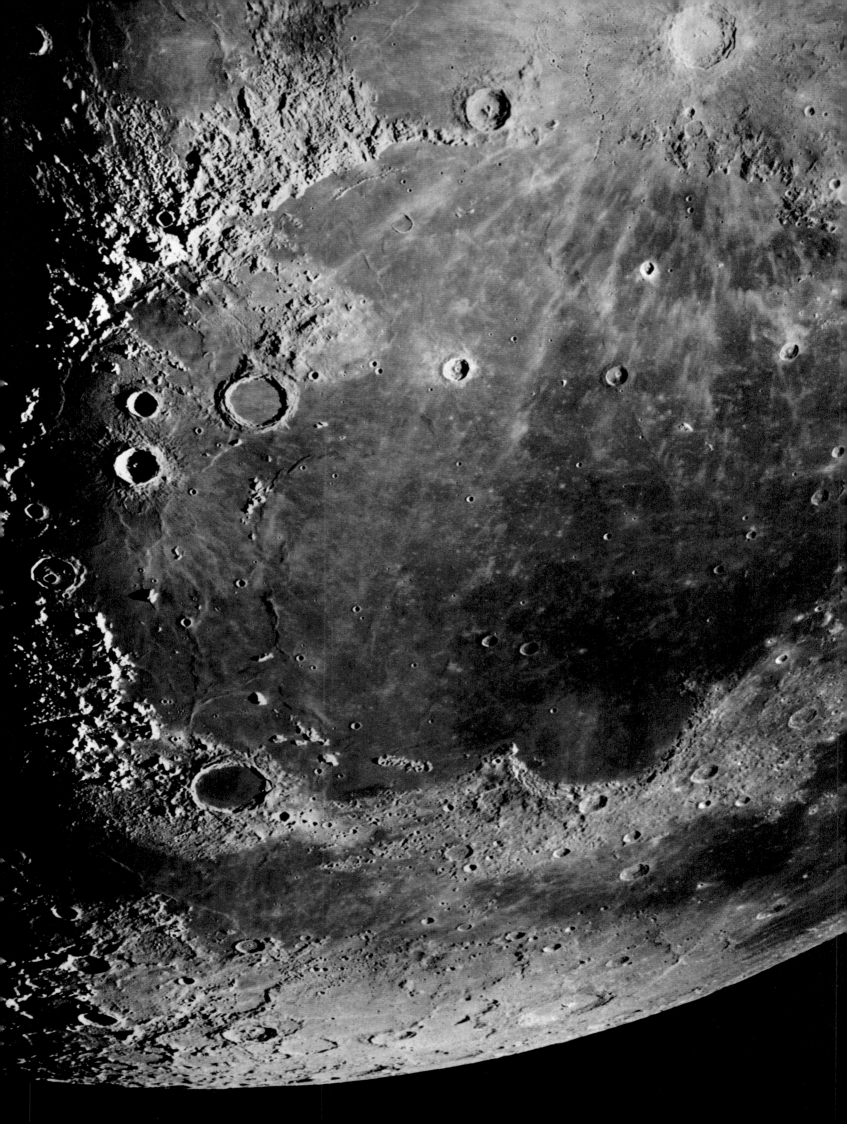

and Gold. According to Baldwin, the volume possessed by celestial bodies striking the Moon so as to hollow out the immense craters is in general grossly overestimated. Since the force gravity on the Moon in six times less, the diameter of a crater created on our satellite is of necessity six times greater than on Earth for the same amount of energy involved. Since also the curvature of the Moon is much more sharply accentuated than that of the Earth, the debris is quite naturally destined to be strewn around considerably further away, and the distance it is thrown is further increased by the absence of atmospheric friction. Furthermore, the velocity attained by the falling meteorites is several tens of kilometres per second, that is to say that it is considerably greater than that of the propagation of longitudinal vibrations in the lunar material. It follows from this that the kinetic energy involved which is suddenly dissipated in heat by the collision is sufficient to vaporize instantaneously the fragments of the meteorite as well as that portion of the ground directly underneath. The effects of such impacts on the Moon are those of a considerable explosion. Enormous breaches can be opened up in this way by relatively small celestial bodies, even if the ground is not particularly plastic. Another important fact is that when the shock wave caused by the collision is propagated at a speed faster than sound, the crater caused by the explosion always takes a circular shape whatever may be the angle of fall ; this detail is a reply to one of the principal objections of the adversaries of the meteoric theory.

In order to support his thesis, Baldwin carried out experiments on a small scale with a view to studying the effects of many types of impact. They showed particularly that a projectile containing no warhead actually does explode if it hits a solid at a speed in excess of 6 kilometres per second.

The presence of a peak or a mountain mass in the centre of many craters still remains today one of the points of controversy between the defenders and the adversaries of the meteoric theory. Baldwin sees two possible explanations : either it is due to the tremendous kinetic energy in the meteorite which, by being transferred to the superficial layers of the Moon, caused some matter to rebound ; or to the explosion initiated underground which continued in such a way that all the debris was not able to be ejected out of the crater. This last hypothesis is all the more plausible since a similar phenomenon is frequently noticed in bomb craters and particularly in the case of time bombs. According to Kuiper, it is rather a question of isostasy, that is to say a spontaneous readjustment of the lunar crust which would re-establish the equilibrium after the explosion, corresponding to the differences in the density of the material. A certain amount of lava would in this way have left the gap opened in the ground and would have caused the central peak.

Origin of the « Seas »

Since the collision of the meteorites on the Moon explains the origin of the craters in a rational manner, why should it not also be the basis for the formation of the maria or « seas » ? This question had already been asked in 1892 by the American scientist G.K. Gilbert. His attention had been attracted by the peculiar orientation of certain rilles which streak the surface of the Mare Imbrium (the Sea of Rains) and he put forward the hypothesis that this sea had been created by the impact of a colossal meteorite. In our day this opinion is not only admitted by a number of scientists but it has been extended to other seas which present similar characteristics. The fact is that eight principal lunar maria are quite circular, but since when Gilbert lived it had not yet been proved that the explosion of a meteorite causes this special shape independent of the angle of impact, there was rather a tendency to consider this state of affairs as an argument against the meteoric theory.

Baldwin envisages the following outline of this astronomic cataclysm. A mass of nickel iron having a diameter of some 15 kilometres landed on the Moon in the north-east and was obliterated in the place which today carries the name of the Sinus Iridum (the Bay of Rainbows). It plunged into the ground, leaving a hole to mark its passage, and raising up a dome above itself ; it then exploded, ejecting blocks of matter and clouds of dust in every direction. In the walls and in the ground, the mountain chains today called the Apennines, the Caucasus, the Alps and the Carpathians rose up towards the south and west ; they were formed for the most part from the material of the initial dome which in the beginning had played the part of a brake. Some separate ejections created isolated mountains such as Pico and Piton. However, because of the tremendous energy liberated at the moment of collision, a general collapse was produced followed by the fusion of the material involved ; an enormous quantity of lava appeared which filled the gap and flowed towards the other existing cavities. The high temperature of this liquid mass allowed it to spread for a hundred hours or so before becoming viscous and since its speed of propagation can be estimated at 24 kilometres per hour, it could have traversed a distance of some 2400 kilometres. In this way, towards the south-east the depressions in the vicinity filled with lava and became the Mare Nubium (Sea of Clouds) and the Oceanus Procellarum (the Ocean of Storms), whilst towards the south-east there occurred the Mare Serenitatis (the Sea of Serenity), Mare Tranquillitatis (Sea of Tranquillity), Mare Fecunditatis (the Sea of Plenty) and the Mare Nectaris (the Sea of Nectar). Although taken as a whole Baldwin's hypothesis is shared by a number of other scientists, certain details have given rise to discussion, such as the flow of the liquid mass towards the other depressions. In fact, there exists no evidence giving any indication of this passage ; therefore several astronomers have tended rather to suppose that these « seas » were created as a consequence of independent, though similar, phenomena occurring at other times. Whatever it may be, according to the appearance of different maria, it seems fairly clear that the general formation of the latter were later than those of the great craters, with the exception, of course, of those possessing a ray system. Kuiper does not think that the liquid material came from the fusion of the meteorite : he believes that we are dealing with a flow emanating from the interior of the Moon which was produced at the time when the Moon's radioactivity had reached its maximum intensity. The heat generated would have been such that the centre would have been in a liquid state almost as far as the surface. The huge meteorites would then have had enough power to perforate the crust and cause oozing of the internal liquid. Before as after this period, meteorites would have hollowed out craters of the classic type.

Gap between the Mare Imbrium and the Mare Serenitatis. — *Photo 37.* — *According to R. B. Baldwin it is through this gap that the lava invaded the Mare Serenitatis.*

(Photo : Pic du Midi Observatory.)
30 May 1944 — 8.50 p.m.
8.55 days.

However, the American scientist Urey does not share this last opinion, for according to him the liquefaction of the core would have considerably reduced the rigidity of the crust and the large formations, such as the mountains, would have disintegrated. He is rather of the opinion, like Baldwin, that the liquid material comes from the liquefaction of the meteorite and from that part of the lunar surface which was struck, but he attributes to the celestial body an appreciably weaker impact velocity, namely 2 to 3 kilometres per second. On the contrary, according to him the mass of the meteorite would be considerably greater, of the order of that of the asteroids ; thus the diameter of the body responsible for the Mare Imbrium would be approximately 200 km. The hypothesis, according to which the maria were created as a consequence of the impact of huge meteorites, explains the presence of furrows on the surface of the Moon. The opinions of Baldwin, Urey and Kuiper are entirely in agreement on this point : the ejected matter which constitutes the blocks scattered in all directions is capable of producing long incisions in the silicate rocks of the Moon. Certain fragments to which these furrows are attributed still remain visible at the extremity of the latter. In every case the visible furrows only make up a small part of a total amount ; in fact, since they cannot be perceived except under special lighting conditions — a very oblique illumination — many of them escape observation.

The clefts and the ridges must be attributed to the existence of phenomena of tension and compression. These may well have arisen owing to successive violent seismic shocks following the impact of meteorites, or as a consequence of the variations in temperature linked with the creation of the great lava fields.

Changes in the Lunar Surface

An account of the origin of the lunar formations would be incomplete if no mention was made of a special point which for generations has excited numerous selenographers and provoked long discussions. From the moment when observations of the Moon were possible by means of instruments, astronomers quite naturally looked to see if there was some proof of life or at least movement on our satellite. Indeed many thought they had discovered changes in the appearance of certain formations and some of these variations became famous. One of the most typical cases is that of the crater Linné whose disappearance was suddenly annonced by the astronomer J. Schmidt in 1866. This crater, which up to that moment had been described as one of the most remarkable objects in the Mare Serenitatis, considering its depth and its diameter, was no longer visible, it was claimed, except as a whitish mark. Several astronomers who following this sensational information had pointed their telescopes to the indicated region confirmed this fact. Today, however, Linné is catalogued as a small crater 900 metres in diameter, surrounded by a wall 30 metres high. Another case, also quite famous, is that of the double crater Messier. About 1830 the two cavities which form it were depicted as twin formations having equivalent diameters and identical shape. Today a distinct difference in depth between the two is noted and whereas one has a rather triangular outline, the second is elliptical. Several other traces of movement were noted by different observers : the interior of the crater Plato was apparently the scene of constant volcanic activity ; the colour of Grimaldi became greenish at times, whilst moving patches could be seen in Eratosthenes.

The majority of modern astronomers are very sceptical about these changes. There is no old document sufficiently accurate which, like a photograph, can be considered to be an indubitable proof of the facts put forward ; all we possess are drawings or descriptions, unfortunately to be treated with caution. Now it is quite obvious that if we think about the totally different appearance that a lunar formation may have according to the manner in which it is illuminated, we are quite right in thinking that these changes are in reality only optical illusions. As long as two photographs of the same place taken under identical conditions of illumination do not irrefutably reveal an established change, the discussion on this thorny subject will no doubt remain open.

It goes without saying that the partisans of the plutonic theory are the most inclined to admit changes on the surface of the Moon since these phenomena would only be, after all, intermittent and normal manifestations of that volcanic activity with which their theories are concerned. These same astronomers are continuing their researches into volcanic theory and certain of them have recently put forward new hypotheses to explain how the explosions on the surface of the Moon could have created the ring formations. According to the Japanese astronomer S. Myamoto, the progressive cooling of our satellite could have caused an extrusion of siliceous magma which would have exploded fiercely on arriving at the outer crust ; the solidification of the lunar sphere would have perhaps been able to give birth to pockets of gas by a concentration of volatile products, bringing about vaporization.

The Oceanus Procellarum. — *Photo 38. — On this photograph which represents an important area of the Oceanus Procellarum (Ocean of Storms) very long ridges may be clearly seen.*
(Photo : Pic du Midi Observatory — age : 9.60 days.)

XIV

THE ATMOSPHERE OF THE MOON

When we look at the Moon, whether it is with the naked eye or with binoculars or a telescope, we are immediately struck by the incomparable sharpness with which all the details stand out. This perfect vision has, besides, been the origin of a very understandable but completely false belief concerning the way in which our sphere might be seen from space. It is generally thought that the first astronauts to land on the Moon will be in a position to look at the Earth, easily finding there all the contours which figure on our maps. Alas, they will only see a disc, obviously much greater and much brighter than the Moon, but irritatingly blurred as a whole. Our world is in fact surrounded by a layer of atmosphere, laden with mist and clouds, which obscures the greatest part of its surface ; such is indeed the case for the planet Venus of which no astronomer has yet been able to discern the slightest portion of land.

Atmosphere and Gravity

Now the Moon has no atmosphere and this state of affairs, it must be added, is in no way due to chance ; it is, on the contrary, the logical consequence of a law of physics. The air is made up of an infinitely large number of gaseous molecules, travelling in all directions and constantly colliding at very great velocities dependent on their nature and their temperature. For the majority of corpuscles, these velocities vary between 200 and 600 metres per second, and for a very small proportion they reach 1400 metres per second, even exceptionally 3500 metres per second. Just like a projectile fired straight up which reaches a great height by virtue of its initial velocity and then falls again, overcome by gravity, the molecules of gas are capable of reaching a great altitude but return to Earth after their ascent into space. Theory tells us, however, that when a body is launched with a sufficiently high speed, the latter is not cancelled out by the effect of gravity except at infinity. In other words, the projectile no longer falls to the ground but goes away from the Earth for ever. At the surface this critical speed is 11,200 metres per second, a value considerably greater than those of all the molecules which go to make up the air, which explains why the Earth steadfastly retains its atmosphere.

The situation is very different at the lunar surface ; there, gravity is six times weaker than on our sphere and as a consequence of this fact the escape velocity is much smaller. It is only 2400 metres per second, but it still remains greater than that which animates the average atmospheric molecule, so that apparently only a small number of these molecules would be destined to escape for ever. However, another phenomenon intervenes here, governed by a law concerning the kinetic energy of gases and the manner in which the relative velocities of their molecules are distributed. After the disappearance of the most rapid corpuscles, the speed of certain others increases and may even reach the critical value ; consequently the escape continues, although it cannot be total except after a relatively long time. Turning to the lunar atmosphere, always supposing of course that our satellite did indeed possess one, it has been estimated that the complete disappearance of the gaseous molecules has required several million years. To tell the truth, if we consider the thousands of millions of years of the existence of the Moon, it can be admitted that the situation of the present day must be already several millions of centuries old.

The results of observations confirm the theoretical conclusions at every point. The sharpness of the lunar edge is especially striking when our satellite passes in front of the Sun, that is to say, during an eclipse. At the time of an occultation, that is, when the Moon obscures a star or a planet, no effect of absorption or of refraction has been discovered ; if there were an atmosphere of any importance, the star instead of being suddenly extinguished would progressively disappear and would be subject to a minute but real displacement owing to the phenomenon of refraction. Besides, the presence of an atmosphere would be the cause of certain twilight effects : for instance, along the terminator the shadows would merge into one another instead of tracing a perfectly clear line of demarcation.

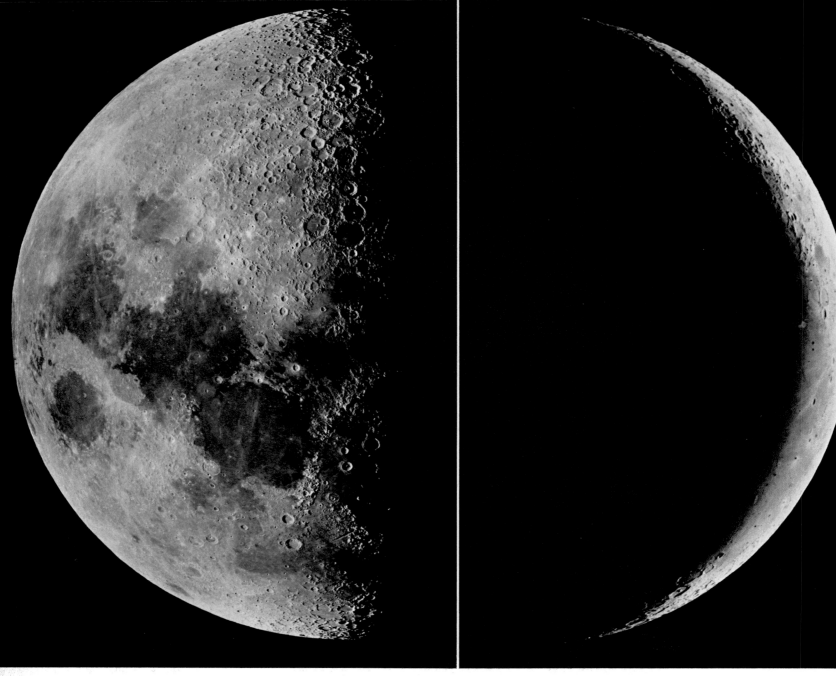

First quarter. — *Photo 39.*   The waning moon. — *Photo 40.*

*On each of these two photos the sharpness of the lunar edge is remarkable, as is also that
of the various formations. This is due to the absence of any atmosphere.*

(Photo : Paris Observatory.)

Degree of Rarefaction

An absolute vacuum does not indeed exist. Even in interplanetary and interstellar space, it is today admitted that there exists an infinitely tenuous matter, the degree of rarefaction of which is of great interest to scientists. In this respect the problem of the lunar atmosphere constitutes one of their preoccupations, for if it is now established that this atmosphere, in the way that we understand it on Earth, is non-existent, it is rather unlikely that the portion of space in the immediate vicinity of the lunar surface would be identical with that which is found some considerable distance away. In fact, what happens to the gaseous material which is probably released from the deep layers of our satellite ? Do the heavy molecules which possess relatively small velocities remain on the surface ? In brief, what is the density and the thickness of this layer of infinitely rarefied air which, despite everything, seems of necessity to surround the Moon ? These are the questions which several astrophysicists are at the present moment trying to resolve.

Amongst the experimental methods used in this respect there is one which relies on the twilight phenomena mentioned earlier on. In 1926 the astronomers Russel, Dugan and Stewart showed that even if the density of the lunar air was 100,000 weaker than that which we breathe, one should still be able to detect against the black background of the sky a twilight glow in the extension of the cusps of the lunar crescent. As they were not able as the result of their experiments to find the slightest trace of this type of light, they felt themselves at liberty to declare the aforementioned value as an upper limit of this density. In 1948 Bernard Lyot and Audouin Dollfus followed the same line of approach, using distinctly more favourable experimental conditions. The detection of the twilight glow can in fact be seriously impaired by stray light which spoils the blackness of the sky near the cusps of the crescent, and thus falsifies the measurement. There are two causes of this detrimental effect : on the one hand, the impurities of the terrestrial atmosphere which through diffusion give rise to a weak haze in the field of the telescope, and on the other, the harmful effect caused by the edges of the diaphragm of the telescope in diffusing and diffracting the incident moonlight. In order to be clear from atmospheric impurity the two French astronomers performed their experiments at the Pic-du-Midi, about 3000 metres above sea level, in the limpid air of the highest observatory in the world. Furthermore, in order to eliminate errors inherent in the instrument, they attached a coronograph to their telescope, an apparatus which had been invented by Lyot himself for the purpose of observing the solar corona by means of an artificial eclipse. Now despite a sensitivity a thousand times greater as a result of these improvements, no trace of the twilight glow was detected ; it was established, therefore, that if a lunar atmosphere existed, its density would be in any case a

The south-east region of the Moon. — Photo 41. — This photograph shows clearly that there is no twilight effect along the terminator, as would have been the case had there been any atmosphere. (Photo : Mount Wilson & Palomar Observatories, 100-inch telescope.)

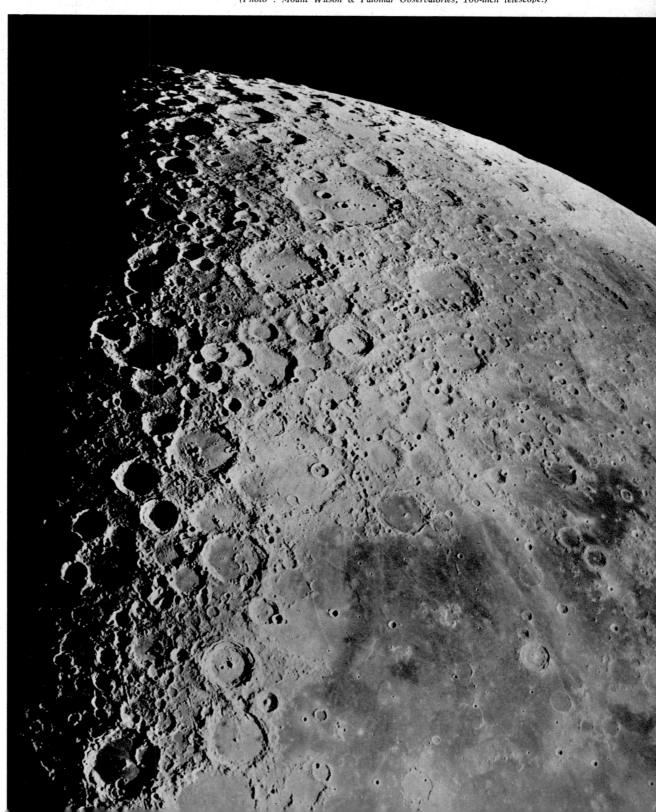

hundred million times weaker than our own. Finally, in 1950, Dollfus again found means of multiplying by a factor of ten the sensitivity of his measurement by utilizing the polarimetric properties of light. As the looked-for glow still did not appear, he was able to conclude that the lunar atmosphere must be at least a thousand million times less dense than the terrestrial atmosphere.

The Consequences of the Absence of Atmosphere

It is difficult to give an immediate account of all the consequences resulting from the absence on the Moon of an atmosphere comparable with our own, for they are as numerous as they are varied. For those concerned with interplanetary travel they naturally constitute the most serious physiological problem, since the absence of air makes, in the first place, any life impossible. When one day men land on the Moon, they will only owe their existence to scientific devices which will allow them to live in a sealed capsule. In any event, we must reject as absurd the suggestion put forward by certain people to create an artificial atmosphere around our satellite ; obviously it would not be able to remain there.

To our misfortune, the Moon is a dreadfully dead body, and the impression of emptiness that will strike its first explorers will be all the more enhanced since our satellite is especially a realm of silence. No noise can be detected, not even the most tremendous explosion, since sound can only be propagated by means of the vibrations of molecules of air.

The action which the Sun exerts on our satellite is totally different from that to which we are accustomed. Whereas the rays sent to us by the Sun are essentially beneficial, on the Moon they are full of treachery. Thanks to a layer of ozone, our atmosphere in fact filters the sunlight and absorbs almost completely the ultra-violet radiations of short wavelength which are particularly harmful and even lethal in strong doses. Similarly it prevents the dangerous corpuscular bombardment from gamma radiation. Now none of this filtration can take place on our satellite which thus receives the complete range of this harmful radiation. Concerning this same light, our atmosphere acts as a diffusing agent and this explains why light remains some considerable time in the evening after the Sun has set, and why it occurs in the morning well in advance of sunrise. On the Moon, however, it vanishes at the very moment when the Sun disappears below the horizon and it only appears at the precise moment of sunrise.

When we look at the question of temperature, the contrast is even more violent : our atmosphere acts as an immense thermal reservoir, the differences between the day and night temperatures being relatively slight. On our satellite, on the contrary, the temperature rises during the day to above 100° C. and at night it falls towards — 150° C., a change taking place in almost as sudden a manner as in the case of sunlight. A similar difference exists, moreover, between any two zones, one exposed to the Sun and the other in shade. A lunar explorer, therefore, who in broad daylight tried to protect himself from the heat of the Sun by hiding in the shade of a mountain or in a crevasse, would be seized instantaneously by a tremendous cold.

Where there is no atmosphere there cannot be water or any other liquid, since in a vacuum all liquid is immediately evaporated. As for water vapour, it could not persist for it would behave just like any other gas. We cannot talk of a lunar climate from any point of view as there are none of the elements which are the basis of climatic conditions, elements such as air, wind, cloud, and rain. It is useless to think of making a fire since no flame can burn without oxygen.

In a completely different domain, our atmosphere exerts another beneficial action : it acts as a shield against meteorites, a role which has already been mentioned earlier on. It is quite certain that for the men who travel to the Moon this permanent bombardment by celestial bodies can only offer serious danger.

Finally, one last point of view, that of the lover of artistic beauty, deserves some attention. Lunar explorers will naturally not have occasion to admire sunsets similar to our own as the vivid colours are due to the air which surrounds us. On the other hand, they will be able to enjoy entirely new spectacles which will certainly be as thrilling. Since the azure colour of the firmament is entirely due to the atmosphere, the lunar sky remains profoundly black, both during the day and the night. In it the stars shine perpetually with no scintillation, since it is once again the atmosphere which prevents us from seeing them during the day by dazzling us with the diffused sunlight ; and likewise it is the atmosphere which causes the phenomenon of scintillation during the night. However we look at it, it is doubtless difficult to imagine the splendour presented by the celestial vault when seen from the Moon. It can only be infinitely more tremendous than that which gratifies our eyes during the clearest nights on a high mountain. Just let us consider the fairy aspect presented to astronauts by the myriads of stars composing our galaxy and particularly that unbelievable stellar concentration known as the Milky Way !

If in a general way the considerations concerning the absence of atmosphere surrounding the Moon must logically lead us to conclude that our satellite is a fundamentally inhospitable body, and if the prospects it has in store for us are scarcely heartening, there is one, however, which is capable of seriously attracting astronomers. For them our atmosphere, laden with moisture and dust, constitutes a constant worry ; what fortune would be theirs, therefore, if they were able to have at their disposal on the Moon an observatory which would give them ideal conditions of visibility if not of comfort !

XV

THE TWO FACES
OF THE MOON

If the proper motions of our satellite, its revolution round the Earth and its rotation on its own axis, places us in the annoying situation of never being able to see more than one side of the Moon, it also has a few surprises in store for those who observe the terrestrial sphere from the Moon. The astronaut who is situated in the region which we call « the unknown face of the Moon » would obviously *never* see the Earth. On the other hand, if he were to remain in the hemisphere which is known to us, he would see it *permanently*, both during the lunar night and during the day. However, he would not have occasion to see the complete disc any more often than we see a full Moon, for the Earth presents itself to its satellite just as the latter to the Earth ; phases continually vary the aspect but with respect to those of the Moon they are displaced by half a cycle. Thus when we see the full Moon it is a new Earth for the lunar observer, and whilst the Moon waxes for us the Earth wanes for him.

A Traveller on the Visible Face of the Moon

The appearance of our sphere in the lunar sky differs in several ways from the familiar appearance of the Moon in our own sky. First of all, it stands out because of its size since the surface area of the terrestrial disc is 13.5 times greater than that of the lunar disc. Besides, whereas the appearance of the Moon is characterized by its clarity and notably by the sharpness of its terminator, this line of demarcation is extremely blurred in the case of the Earth. In fact, the atmosphere causes a considerable diffusion of light, and between the light and dark zones gives rise to a relatively wide band where the light merges imperceptibly into shadow. Furthermore, this same atmosphere prevents the terrestrial sphere from merging entirely into the dark sky during the period of the new Earth, such as happens during a new Moon. Illuminated from behind by the Sun, it traces around the Earth a narrow shining ring, similar to that mentioned earlier in the description of a total eclipse of the Moon observed from the satellite itself (Fig. 47).

Finally — and this is the immediate consequence of the proper motion of the Moon — the Earth remains in the vault of heaven in an almost unchanging position depending only on the place of observation. Almost entirely devoid of apparent motion, it reigns eternally in state in the same place whilst behind it the stars revolve as they do in our sky. This rotation is very much slower since a complete circle takes the time of a sidereal revolution of the Moon, namely 27 ⅓ days. As for the Sun, it also participates in the turning motion but with even less speed, for in order to accomplish this same orbit it takes the time necessary for a synodic revolution, that is to say 29 ½ days.

One detail which is particularly interesting is that the motions peculiar to our satellite place the lunar observer opposite a terrestrial sphere which, although appearing stationary in space, nevertheless turns on its own axis. Unfortunately it is quite probable that he will find this further motion difficult to detect, for the clouds and

Fig. 47. — The « new Earth » seen from the Moon. The « new Earth » as seen from the Moon is a completely black disc surrounded by a shining corona which is its atmosphere illuminated from behind.

87

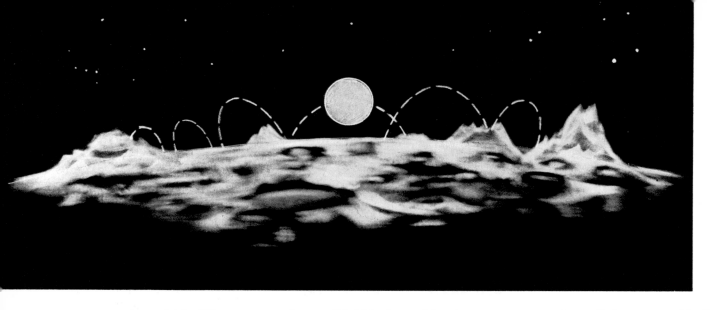

Fig. 48. — Apparent motion of the Earth on the lunar horizon. *An observer, situated on the Moon in a place within the 18 % of the surface which is alternately hidden and visible from us, would see the Earth rise and set in turn according to the libration cycle. As this libration is due to many causes the apparent trajectories of the Earth follow quite complicated paths resembling arcs based on the horizon.*

mists which fill our atmosphere will hide from his view a very great part of the geographical contours. This annoying characteristic of our atmosphere will not only considerably reduce the enchantment which he will have in the contemplation of the Earth from the Moon but will deprive him of a valuable means of measuring the passage of time.

One final question may be asked : how will the phenomenon of libration show itself when seen from our satellite ? The reply which in fact is largely self-explanatory is partially given by the expression used above : « an almost unchanging position ». If libration gives us the impression that the Moon is oscillating slightly, then on the other hand, the Earth seen from the Moon seems to describe in the sky small closed loops following the rhythm of libration. These paths have rather irregular shapes and are of slight extent since they correspond to the limits of libration, that is twice 7° 54' in the east-west direction, and twice 6° 50' in the north-south direction. Therefore, for an explorer who is not furnished with instruments and who is situated in the centre of the region forming the 41 per cent of the lunar surface which is perpetually visible from the Earth, these motions of our sphere will be scarcely perceptible. But for an astronaut situated at a point on the 18 per cent of the surface alternately hidden and visible, the situation will be quite different : to him the Earth would rise and set in turn at a frequency governed by the libration, and the paths which it would trace in the sky would resemble arcs of various shapes, based on the horizon (Fig. 48).

Fig. 49. — Rough map of the other face of the Moon. — *This map has been drawn by the Academy of Sciences of the U.S.S.R. immediately after the study of numerous photographs taken by Lunik III. The names of various lunar formations (seas, craters, mountains) have been chosen by the Praesidium of the Academy of Sciences of the U.S.S.R. and submitted to the International Astronomical Union.*
(In the second part of this book — the Atlas — there is a considerably more detailed map.)

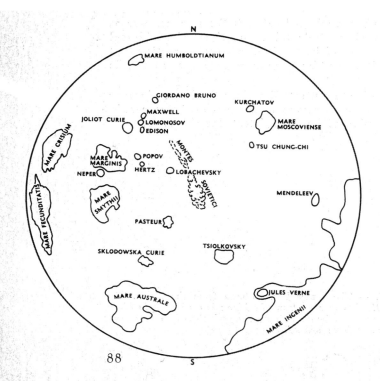

The Structure of the Unknown Side

From the time some 350 years ago when astronomers discovered the changeless nature of the appearance of the Moon, mankind being curious has quite naturally wondered about the nature of the invisible face, and many imaginative minds have not been slow to find a thousand reasons for stating that it must have a completely different appearance. At first it seems absurd to think that the direction in which the Moon lies with respect to the Earth, and which is always the same, can be the basis of any difference in structure or in relief between the two faces. However, it is not quite so simple as that, for there is one not inconceivable celestial phenomenon in which the Earth plays an important part and which only affects one and the same side of our satellite : the eclipse of the Moon. Certain scientists have seen in this fact the possible cause of a separate evolution for each of the two hemispheres in question. If we consider that the variations in temperature which occur at the surface of the Moon during such eclipses take place during a period of time considerably shorter than that which elapses between the lunar days and nights and further, that considered on the scale of geological time, the frequency of the occurrence of eclipses is extremely great, we are right in supposing that the effects of erosion are more profound on the visible side than on the other. As has been said earlier on, this question has recently received the attention of Dollfus who has calculated the stresses affecting the lunar rocks and has finally contested the likelihood of the suggested hypothesis. There would not, therefore, seem to be any reason why the nature of the lunar surface should not be appreciably the same at all points.

The Photograph of the Other Face of the Moon

A great step towards the solution of this difficult and intriguing problem was taken in October 1959, thanks to the sensational exploit performed by Lunik III which carried out the first journey round our satellite. Although the photographs taken during this memorable extra-terrestrial journey did not warrant any pronouncements by astronomers on the details characterizing the invisible face of the Moon, nevertheless they allowed provisional maps presenting a real interest to be drawn up (Fig. 49). The least that can be said is that the results obtained are extraordinary if we consider the multiplicity and the magnitude of the difficulties which it was necessary to overcome.

The photographs were taken at the moment when the Sun was exactly behind the space probe carrying the apparatus ; they show consequently the drawbacks which characterise the views which we know of the full Moon, namely a lack of relief. Doubtless we may wonder why the scientists involved in this experiment did not rather choose an oblique illumination which would have brought out the contrasts. The answer is simple : the side illumination only occurs at the quarters and in order to benefit from the advantages which it offers it would have been necessary to take two series of photographs, one each quarter. As this solution implies a delay of 14 days between the two operations, it could not practically have been carried out except by the successive launching of two rockets. However, another difficulty would then have added to the problem : the well-nigh impossibility of realising the respective positions of the Sun, the Earth and the Moon which determine the ideal moment of launch ; in fact, these are far from being repeated every 14 days. Lunik III carried a camera provided with two lenses : one having a focal length of 200 mm to be used for taking a complete picture of the lunar disc : whilst the other, with a focal length of 500 mm, was designed for photographs of greater resolution. The correct aim of the camera was ensured by a system of orientation depending on the use of optical sensors, mechanisms sensitive to light similar to the well-known photoelectric cell (Fig. 50).

At a predetermined moment — the space probe was then at a distance of between 60,000 and 70,000 kilometres from the Moon and at a point on the straight line joining our satellite to the Sun — a signal transmitted

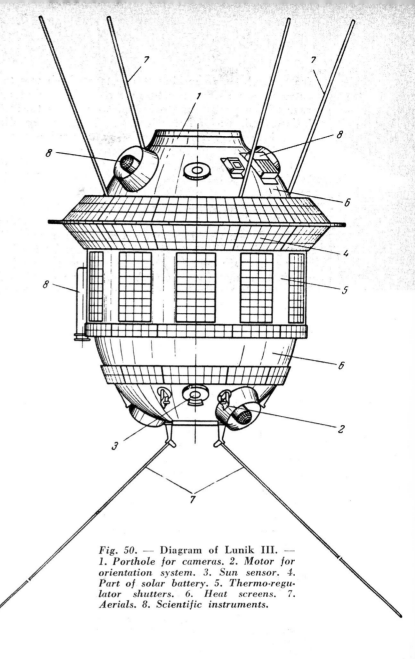

Fig. 50. — Diagram of Lunik III. — 1. Porthole for cameras. 2. Motor for orientation system. 3. Sun sensor. 4. Part of solar battery. 5. Thermo-regulator shutters. 6. Heat screens. 7. Aerials. 8. Scientific instruments.

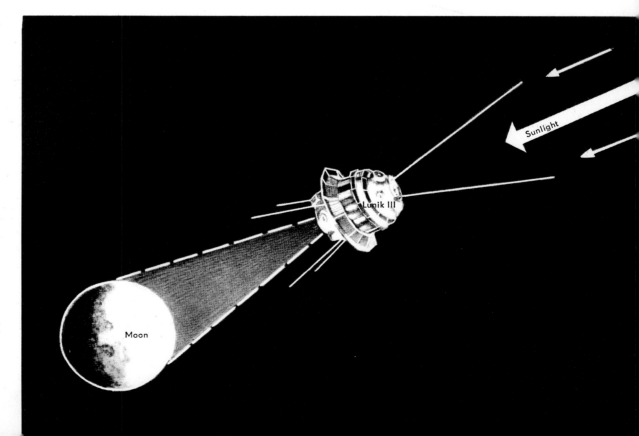

Fig. 51. — Position of Lunik III when taking photographs.

from Earth set in motion the system which was to ensure the correct aim. By means of electronic circuits a retro motor halted the tumbling of the rocket around its centre of gravity. The optical sensors placed in the rear of the probe then oriented themselves towards the Sun in such a way that the camera, fixed in its position beforehand, was automatically sighted in the direction of the Moon. Finally, a highly accurate optical device came into play, its purpose being to perfect the orientation and to prevent the Earth as it came into the field of vision from spoiling the photograph by its own reflected light. Thanks to the action of this device, the lens could only be triggered when the Moon alone was in the field of the camera (Fig. 51). Photographs were taken during about 40 minutes, after which the orientation system ceased to operate, thus causing the recommencement of the tumbling.

The film used in the camera was of standard size, 35 mm, but its composition had been studied in great detail in order that it should resist the high temperatures and the harmful effects of cosmic rays. After exposure it passed into the development chamber, a part of the installation designed to function under special conditions and particularly that of weightlessness. There it was developed, fixed and then dried. The second series of operations was now ready to take place : the television transmission of the photographs towards the Earth. To effect this new operation, the technique employed was that used at the present moment on Earth, augmented by methods particular to automation. Thus, for example, since nothing was known in advance concerning the density of these negatives and the contrast presented by the pictures, it was necessary to add to the transmitting apparatus a regulating system capable of automatically compensating for the variations in opacity and contrast.

The release of the transmission of the pictures by television was remotely controlled by a station on Earth ; the scientists could thus choose the moment which they considered the most favourable. In fact, the transmission took place several times at different distances from our sphere ; the maximum separation was 470,000 kilometres. The aerials carried by the space probe were of an omni-directional type, that is to say, they had the property of transmitting the same intensity in every direction. As a result of this there was an enormous loss of the small energy available, and one might be led to believe that in order to concentrate this towards the only interested place, namely the Earth, it would have been more advantageous to use so-called uni-directional aerials. Unfortunately their use had to be excluded as a result of the unavoidable motion of the rocket which continually varied the orientation of its various elements.

As has already been said, the aim of the technicians who launched Lunik III was to obtain the most extensive picture of the other side of the Moon at the risk of sacrificing the details presented by different formations. In fact, the photographs taken covered approximately 70 per cent of the unknown surface and they coincided with the eastern part of the visible hemisphere thanks to a certain amount of overlap. The Mare Crisium is in this respect the most important formation which clearly appears both on the classical picture of the full Moon and on the new photographs. Without a doubt, the time is not very far off when new journeys into space will be undertaken allowing photographs to be taken of this mysterious region under different conditions of illumination.

The Moon's other face. — *Photo 42. — The dotted line forms the boundary between the known and unknown faces of the Moon. The large black spot on the left of this line, half way up the photograph, is the Mare Crisium. The two spots crossed by the line are respectively from top to bottom the Mare Marginalis and the Mare Smythii.* (Photo taken by Lunik III.)

Detail of the unknown face. — *Photo 43. — (Photo taken by Lunik III.)*

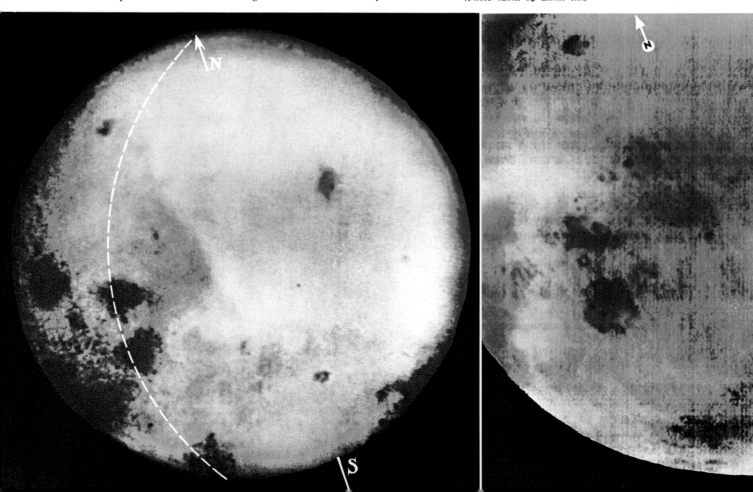

XVI

THE SHAPE
OF THE SELENOID

The Selenoid

Is the Moon a perfect sphere ? This is a question which would not seem to give ground for much discussion for, after all that has been said on the subject, it seems clear that an immediate reply could be given in the affirmative. And yet it is a fact recognized today that the Moon is not strictly spherical ; very small differences exist between the lengths of the diameters measured in different directions with a result that the lunar disc is not, in fact, a perfect circle. In other words, if we were able to observe it from different points in space, we would see it each time with a very slightly different outline.

To these variations in the average profile must be added others even smaller which are due entirely to irregularities of the surface and which have, therefore, a purely local character. The surface of the Moon is, as we know, far from being smooth ; between the seas and the summits of the mountains, as between the centre of the craters and walls, the difference in level is of the order of several kilometres. Besides, a curious chance has decided that the highest peaks, those of the Leibnitz mountains, should be situated quite near the limb. However, in any case, we are only dealing with variations representing, relatively speaking, 1 to 2/1,000 of the lunar diameter.

Until recently the variations which affected the average profile and also the local profile were generally neglected, for the methods of observation did not involve the accuracy necessary to justify taking them into consideration. One example may illustrate this fact. In order to determine the time when a star passes a given point in the sky, the astronomer records the event, and this procedure brings into play a human element, the reaction time peculiar to the observer. Now this delay which is called the *observer's personal equation* differs from one individual to the next. Today, as a result of the use of new methods and apparatus, this lack of precision has been eliminated.

In fact, it is possible nowadays to record the most minute motions of the heavenly bodies and to determine the slightest irregularity in their shape. There is no need to add that these results could not have been obtained except with apparatus of extreme accuracy. At the present day celestial mechanics involves the tiniest details and as regards the Moon in particular it calls for a knowledge of the exact position of its centre of gravity in the sky, and that means its real shape.

Under such circumstances the moments of the occultation of a star behind the Moon as well as the times of contact during an eclipse must be able to be determined in a precise fashion. Now the observation of an occultation always involves the lunar edge with its continuously jagged outline. The precise moment when the star disappears depends consequently on the exact place where contact is made. Previously this detail was somewhat neglected because the possible errors resulting from the method used were of the same order of magnitude as those which could be imputed to the personal equation of the observer. The astronomer behaved, in fact, as he still does today concerning that other phenomenon resulting from the irregularities of the lunar profile, namely Baily's beads which have been discussed in the chapter on eclipses of the Sun. He is content merely to record the existence of this rosary of luminous points which appears round the lunar disc during total and annular eclipses of the Sun, for the time has not yet come when he can predict the exact place and moment of their appearance.

In the exact measurement of eclipses the same problem is posed ; the determination of contact between the solar and lunar discs is seriously affected by the irregularity of the profile of the Moon, and the errors between the calculated time and the observed time can in certain cases be as much as a second. Nowadays this interval of time is considered as completely inadmissible. In short, just as the Earth has been and continues to be the object of research concerning its shape, and from this point of view is known under the name of *geoid*, so the Moon is at the present day the object of extremely accurate studies in this respect and has received the particular name of *selenoid*.

The Local Lunar Profile

The study of the lunar profile is considerably more complex than is generally imagined. The reasons for the difficulties encountered are numerous, amongst which mention must first be made of the phases of the Moon. In fact, it is seldom that our satellite can be seen in its entirety, and even at the moment of full Moon we must deplore the rather unsatisfactory illumination which certain portions of the limb receive. Besides, the correlation of pictures taken at the time of first or last quarter or when simply a crescent is visible is extraordinarily difficult.

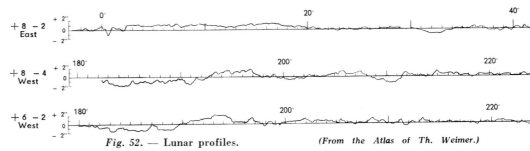

Fig. 52. — Lunar profiles. (From the Atlas of Th. Weimer.)

Photo 44. — *This photograph taken during the eclipse of the Sun of 15th February 1961 shows clearly the irregularities of the Moon's edge silhouetted by the Sun. To distinguish them better, place the eye close to the photograph and look along the lunar profile.*
(Photo : J. Dommanget — Royal Observatory of Belgium.)

Obviously eclipses provide much better conditions but unfortunately these are of too short a duration. Another cause of difficulty lies in the phenomena of libration. The latter, which involve three distinct aspects as we have seen, are exclusively apparent motions ; they have been grouped under their common designation of *optical librations*, in order to distinguish them from a fourth libration very much weaker, which is an absolute or real motion of the Moon. In fact, it is the study of this *physical libration* which has brought to light the lack of homogeneity in the distribution of mass in the interior of our satellite, and has explained its non-spherical shape. The way in which the Moon behaves in this respect resembles a little that of the Kelly doll sitting on its relatively heavy sphere which forces it to remain vertical. As soon as it is moved from its position of equilibrium, it comes back very quickly after carrying out a number of oscillations. If, as is now supposed, the distribution of lunar mass is not spherical, our satellite has only one position of equilibrium. Its eccentricity moves it periodically from this unique position towards which it ceaselessly tends to return, oscillating very slightly. This physical libration can, of course, only be measured with instruments of extreme accuracy for it does not exceed a few minutes of arc. In order to add the corrections necessitated by the irregularities of the limbs of the Moon to the results of the observations carried out on them, the French astronomer Weimer has drawn up a considerable number of profiles each one of which represents the appearance of the limb for successive values of libration. This task required the preliminary examination of an enormous quantity of photographs of the limb and a knowledge of the exact moment of exposure, since it was necessary to know all the correlated astronomical elements. Consequently a complete study of physical libration was involved since it adds its effects to the optical librations. This made necessary the precise knowledge of the co-ordinates of a certain number of lunar formations, for example, the craters. Further, it was advisable to determine the maximum admissible angular separation between two consecutive profiles capable of giving the two pictures a general appearance which was sufficiently alike to enable an eventual interpolation to be easily made. The value of this separation, which depends on the radius of curvature of the Moon and on the height of the mountains, was fixed at 2°. Finally, seeing that on the Moon there is no reference point such as sea level on Earth, it was necessary to define one quite arbitrarily for each contour envisaged to which the irregularities of various profiles could be referred.

Using a method perfected by himself as well as an apparatus specially designed to measure the photograph, to magnify the irregularities and to re-establish the corrected contours, Weimer produced no less than 144 lunar profiles (Fig. 52). Besides, he concluded that the lengthening of the diameter of the Moon, a lengthening which had been already considered some time before as being in the direction of the Earth, was of about 6 kilometres. This same problem was studied, but using different methods, by Koziel, a Polish astronomer, and Senouque, a French physicist. According to the latter the deformation is probably only about 1 kilometre.

Whatever the result may be, unfortunately no confirmation of this hypothesis can be provided by a process of direct measurement since it would be necessary to observe our satellite « from the side », if we can use that expression. No doubt we can hope that this verification will be possible one day when an interplanetary rocket succeeds in taking a photograph of the lunar disc at a suitable angle. And it will be necessary for the picture to lend itself to study for the differences in distance involved are infinitely small. It is quite obvious that the process of transmitting photographs by television such as was used by Lunik III causes too much distortion and a consequent lack of accuracy to permit the desired inspection. This therefore requires that the photo taken by the rocket should arrive untouched in the hands of those who wish to study it.

The Average Lunar Profile

The study of the average profile of the Moon had already been undertaken at the beginning of this century by R.P. Chevalier, who, at the Observatory of Zo-Sê in China, carried out some very interesting observations. During the total eclipses of the Moon on the 15th September 1913 and the 4th September 1914, he took photographs of the lunar disc and the study of these led him to state that the polar diameter must be greater than the equatorial diameter. Unfortunately his method presents the grave defect of not being utilizable except during eclipses. On the other hand, the Belgian astronomer Dommanget has just completed another process which is independent of this constraint ; the photographs which he studies can in fact be taken at any time. The results obtained up to the moment seem indeed to confirm Chevalier's conclusions : the major axis of the lunar disc such as we see it from our terrestrial observatory would pass through the region of the crater Tycho.

Second Part

ATLAS

INDEX OF LUNAR FORMATIONS

The figures indicate the plates on which the various formations appear. Those in heavy type indicate the plates where a short description of the formation may be found. The figures in parentheses indicate that the formation, being in the libration zone, is only shown on the accompanying map on which the names of the various features are inscribed. All the names are those approved by the International Astronomical Union.

95

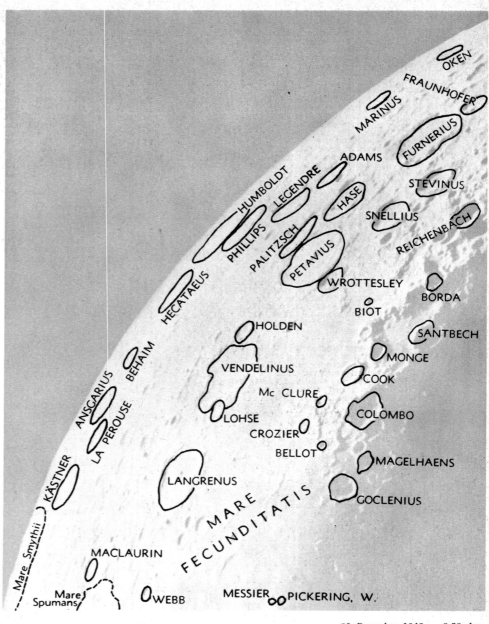

30 December 1943 — 3.53 days.

PLATE 1

FEATURES OF NOTE

COLOMBO. Ring formation 80 km in diameter rather irregular. Breached in the north-east by a crater 40 km wide. Floor comprises a hillock, ridges and craterlets.

FRAUNHOFER. Crater 50 km wide and 1500 m deep. Walls are terraced and broken by a few craters.

FURNERIUS. Walled plain 125 km across. Terraced walls rising to 3500 m. Gap in the south. Interior contains numerous craters and is crossed by a cleft.

HASE. Large crater with walls rising to 2000 m. Craterlets and numerous pits on the slopes and floor.

PETAVIUS 21 May 1960 — 2000 hrs — Photo 45.

PALITZSCH. Irregular formation, 100 km long and 30 km wide, formed by the juxtaposition of several craters.

PETAVIUS. Very old ring worn down by erosion. Stands out very clearly at the beginning of the lunation, then very quickly becomes less distinct. Diameter 160 km. Walls double in places, height varying between 2000 and 3500 m. Central mountain group 1700 m high. Numerous ridges radiating from the walls. Interior mound cut diametrically by a deep cleft. Lips joined together on one side, almost obliterating the fault, both halves drifting forward and thus forming a cliff.

SNELLIUS & STEVINUS. Two similar rings 80 km wide with a central peak. Cleft joining both formations.

VENDELINUS. An enormous formation, very irregular, extending over 150 km from north to south. Considerably broken up by erosion. Floor and walls pitted with craters.

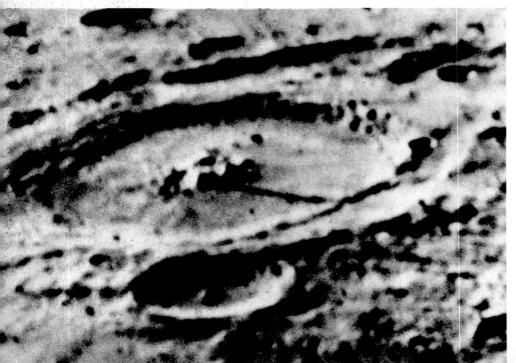

98

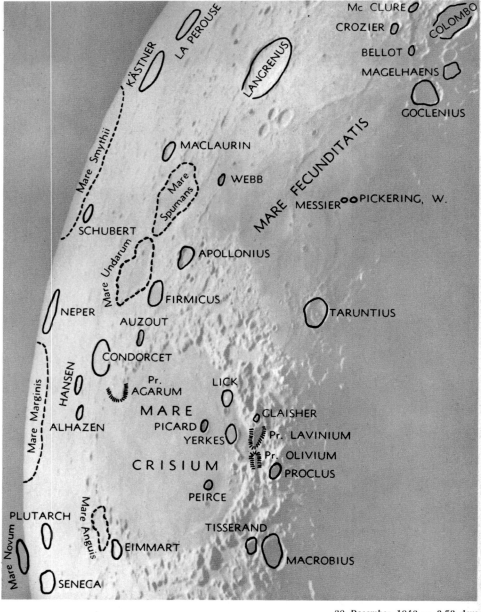

30 December 1943 — 3.53 days.

PLATE 2

FEATURES OF NOTE

CONDORCET. Ring 75 km in diameter. Terraced walls reaching 2400 m.

MARE CRISIUM. Perceptibly circular « sea ». Mean diameter 500 km. Strewn with ridges and craters, of which the most important, Picard, has a diameter of 33 km and walls of 1500 m.

LANGRENUS 25 May 1960 — 2030 hrs — Photo 46.

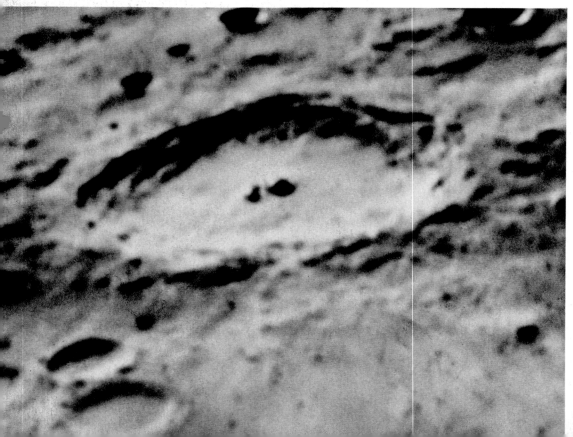

MARE FECUNDITATIS. A dark plain extending 1000 km from north to south and 700 km from east to west. Strewn with ridges and craters.

LANGRENUS. A vast walled plain 140 km in diameter. Very irregular edges covered with numerous craters, reaching 2500 m in the east. Rather narrow terraces. A twin-peaked central mountain group, one of the peaks rising to 1000 m.

MARE SMYTHII & MARE MARGINIS. Two formations near the limb, alternately hidden and revealed by libration. They appear on the photographs taken by Lunik III to have a shape and dimensions similar to the Mare Crisium.

MESSIER. Deep small crater 15 km across. Made famous by changes which W. Pickering claimed to have seen, but which are probably due solely to variations in illumination.

100

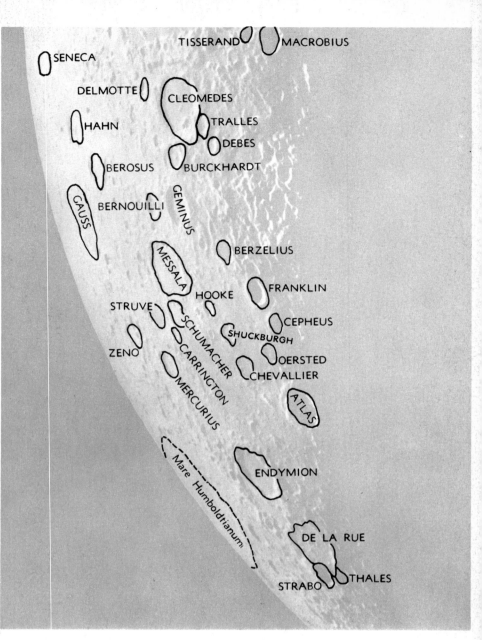

30 December 1943 — 3.54 days.

PLATE 3

FEATURES OF NOTE

BURCKHARDT. A ring of rather peculiar shape, diameter 50 km, overlapping other craters. Massive walls reaching 4000 m in the east. A small hill in the centre. Small craters on the outer slopes of the walls.

ENDYMION 29 May 1960 — 2025 hrs — Photo 47.

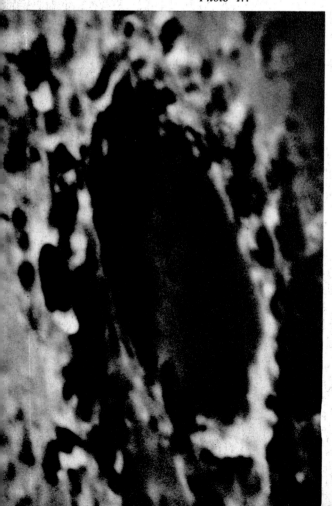

CLEOMEDES. A great ring, 130 km in diameter. A massive wall with peaks rising to between 2500 and 2700 m. The floor crossed by numerous clefts and covered with a few craters. Central mountain group. The crater Tralles intrudes in the north-east.

DE LA RUE. A very ancient and enormous formation of completely irregular outline. A low wall, broken in numerous places. Covered with craters and ridges. Indented on the north by the two craters Strabo and Thales.

ENDYMION. An enormous crater 125 km in diameter with a very dark smooth floor ; some white patches and several craterlets. Very high walls, 4500 m in the west, higher in the north.

GAUSS. A vast walled plain 175 km across. High walls. Central mountain group in the interior as well as some very old craters.

GEMINUS. Crater 90 km in diameter. Terraced wall rising to 4500 m.

MARE HUMBOLDTIANUM. A sea situated quite close to the limb and consequently often hidden by libration. Very high peaks along its western edge, some reaching a height of almost 5000 m.

MESSALA. Large walled plain of 115 km in diameter. Not a high wall. Floor covered with craterlets and broken fragments.

102

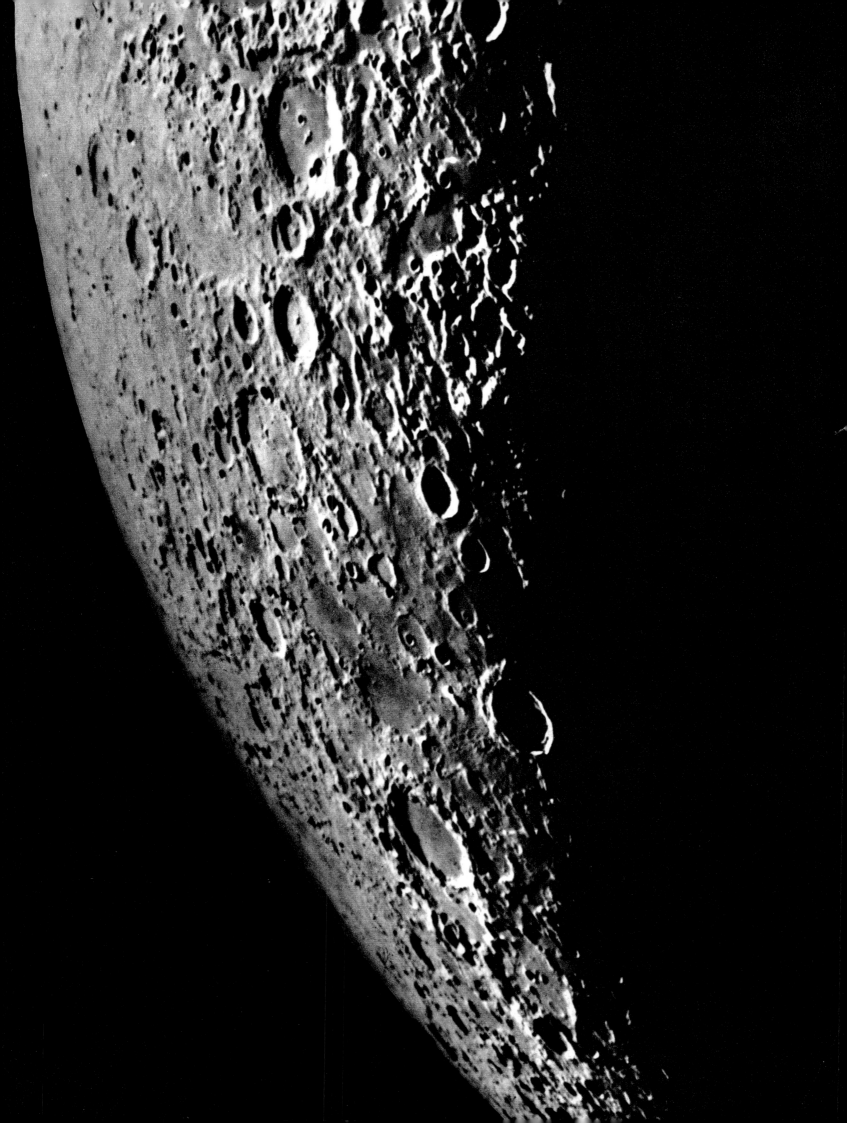

PLATE 4

FEATURES OF NOTE

FABRICIUS. Crater 90 km in diameter. Wall rising to 2500 m. Central mountain. Considerably encroaches on Janssen.

FRACASTORIUS. Example of a very old ring over which has poured the lava from a neighbouring sea (M. Nectaris). The north wall has disappeared, through fusion due to the lava flow. Diameter 100 km. Remains of a central mountain group, but of little altitude. Numerous craters on the floor and walls.

HAGECIUS. Crater 75 km in diameter partially overlapped by other craters.

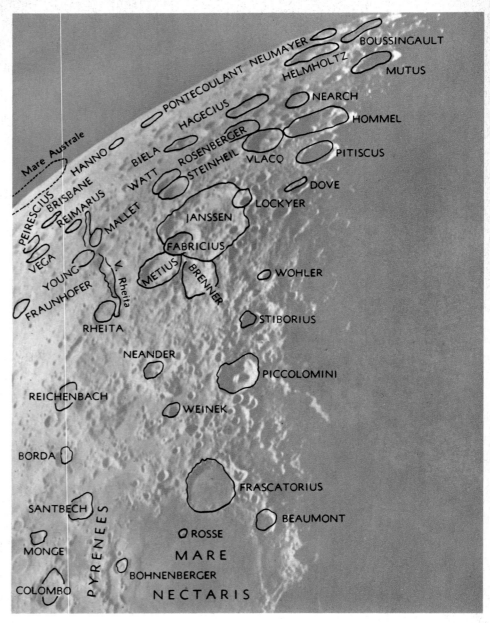

29 March 1944 — 5.35 days.

FRACASTORIUS 30 May 1960 — 2000 hrs — Photo 48.

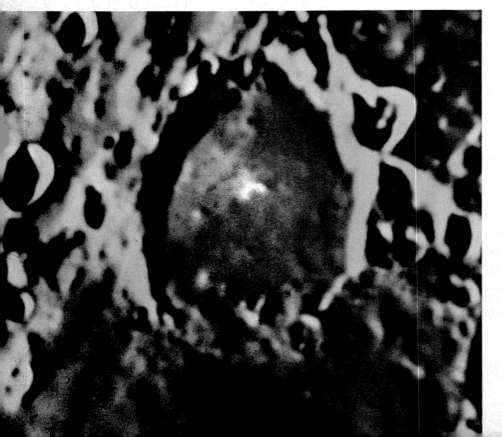

HELMHOLTZ. Crater 100 km across. High walls. Double mountain group.

HOMMEL. Vast depression 120 km in diameter on which several craters intrude. The interior floor contains ridges, craterlets and traces of ring formations.

JANSSEN. An immense old many-sided formation over 100 km across. Wall indented by numerous craters. Floor very uneven with ridges, clefts and craters.

METIUS. Crater 80 km in diameter. Terraced wall with a peak of 4000 m. Central hill.

RHEITA VALLEY. A trough 180 km long and with a maximum width of 24 km. At its northern end it encroaches on the crater Rheita, and at the south it emerges into the crater Mallet.

ROSENBERGER. Crater 80 km in diameter. Central hill. Ridges and clefts.

STEINHEIL & WATT. Two great rings lying side by side, containing ridges and clefts. Terraced wall rising to a height of 3300 m.

104

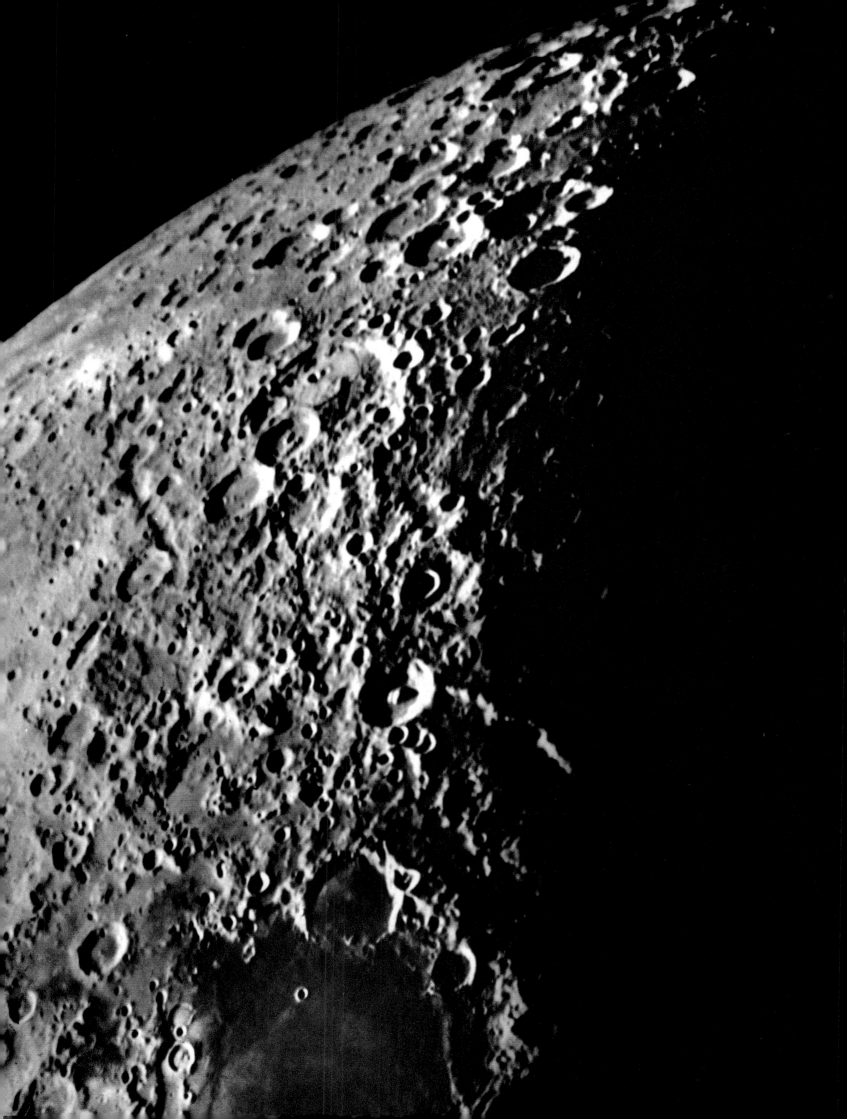

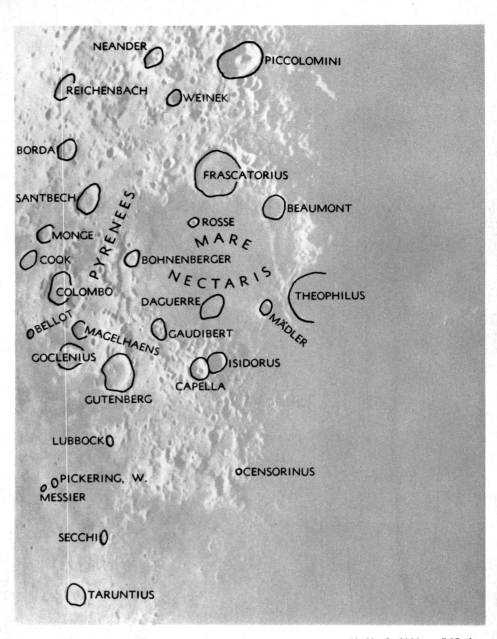

29 March 1944 — 5.35 days.

PLATE 5

FEATURES OF NOTE

CAPELLA & ISIDORUS. Two craters 50 km in diameter, the first having intruded into the second. Central hill in Capella.

TARUNTIUS 29 May 1960 — Photo 49.

GOCLENIUS. Crater 50 km in diameter. Wall 1500 m high, ruined in numerous places. Central hill and numerous clefts.

GUTENBERG. Crater 65 km across. The north-west edge overlapped by a crater some 20 km in diameter. Southern wall shows a number of gaps. Central hill.

MARE NECTARIS. An appreciably square area some 300 km on each side. Rough surface near the east with numerous ridges, hills and craterlets. A prominent arête joins Theophilus to Beaumont. Numerous ridges radiate from Rosse together with a cleft.

PICCOLOMINI. Deep crater 90 km in diameter. Very high terraced walls from which rise up peaks of 4500 m. Central hill.

PYRENEES. Chain of mountains of low altitude, the highest peak reaching 3500 m.

SANTBECH. Crater 70 km in diameter. High walls with peaks from 3000 to 4500 m.

TARUNTIUS. A remarkable type of crater with a filled interior showing a particularly distorted structure. Diameter 60 km. The interior has a discontinuity one third of the way from its centre. The central ring-shaped portion is displaced vertically. Numerous hills and ridges in the interior. Narrow wall reaching 1000 m covered with several craterlets. Central mountain group.

106

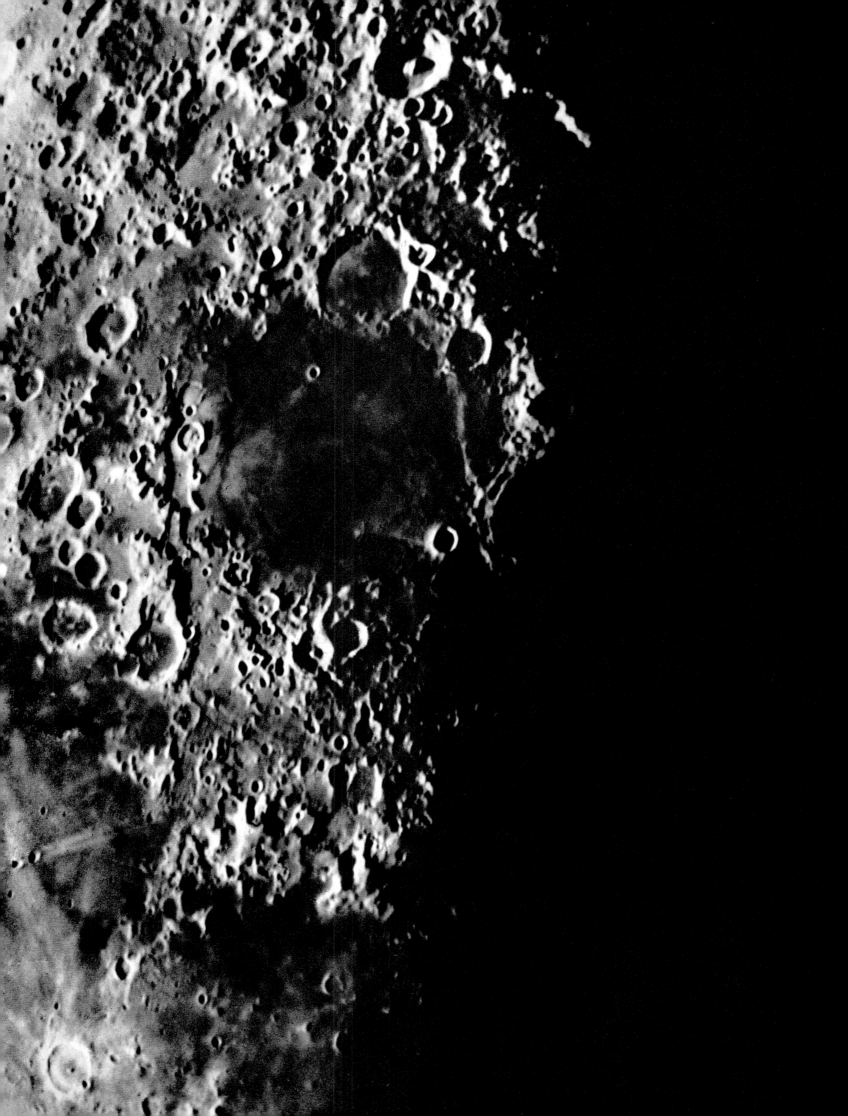

PLATE 6

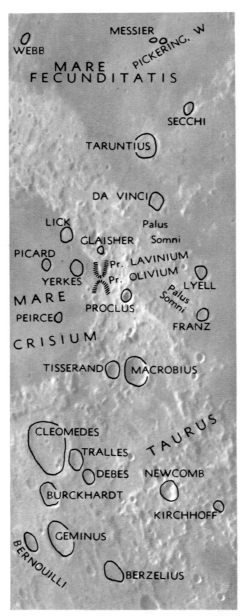

MESSIER

WEBB

PICKERING. W

MARE
FECUNDITATIS

SECCHI

TARUNTIUS

DA VINCI

LICK   Palus
      Somni
GLAISHER

PICARD   Pr. LAVINIUM

YERKES   Pr. OLIVIUM

        Palus   LYELL
        Somni
MARE

PEIRCE   PROCLUS

                    FRANZ

CRISIUM

TISSERAND   MACROBIUS

CLEOMEDES

            TRALLES   TAURUS

        DEBES   NEWCOMB

BURCKHARDT

            KIRCHHOFF

GEMINUS

BERNOUILLI   BERZELIUS

29 March 1944 — 5.35 days.

108

PLATE 7

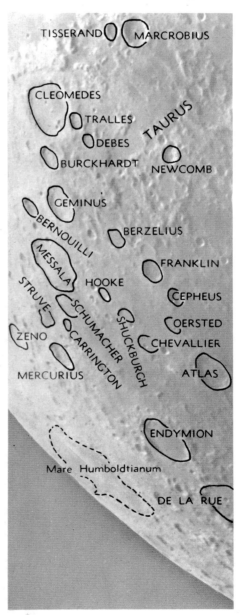

29 March 1944 — 5.35 days.

PLATE 8

FEATURES OF NOTE

BAROCIUS. Crater 80 km in diameter. Walls broken in many places rising to 3500 m.

CLAIRAUT. Old crater 150 km in diameter. Very misshapen owing to superimposition of two quite large craters on it.

FARADAY. Very irregular formation markedly intruding on the walls of Stöfler and itself encroached upon by other craters.

HERACLITUS & LICETUS. Two intercommunicating ringed plains of very distorted outline. Overlapped in places by numerous varied formations. Very high walls.

PONTECOULANT HAGECIUS NEUMAYER
BIELA HELMHOLTZ BOUSSINGAULT SIMPELIUS
ROSENBERGER NEARCH MUTUS MANZINUS PENTLAND
WATT STEINHEIL VLACQ HOMMEL TANNERUS KINAU ZACH
JANSSEN LOCKYER ASCLEPI JACOBI LILIUS
FABRICIUS PITISCUS IDELER BACO
DOVE BREISLAK CUVIER
BRENNER SPALLANZANI BAROCIUS CLAIRAUT HERACLITUS
WÖHLER NICOLAI LICETUS
STIBORIUS RICCIUS BÜSCHING MAUROLYCUS FARADAY
LINDENAU RABBI LEVI BUCH STÖFLER
ROTHMANN CELSIUS GEMMA FRISIUS FERNELIUS
ZAGUT KAISER
WILKINS GOODACRE NONIUS
ALTAI POISSON WALTER
PONS PONTANUS ALIACENSIS
POLYBIUS REGIOMONTANUS
FERMAT SACROBOSCO APIANUS WERNER
SCARP KRUSENSTERN
AZOPHI BLANCHINUS PURBACH
CATHARINA ABENEZRA PLAYFAIR DELAUNAY LA CAILLE
TACITUS GEBER DONATI FAYE
ALMANON
KANT AIRY ARZACHEL
ABULFEDA ARGELANDER
DESCARTES BURNHAM VOGEL

3 January 1944 — 7.54 days.

MAUROLYCUS-STÖFLER Region — Photo 50.

MAUROLYCUS. One of the oldest rings of this region. Diameter exceeds 200 km. In the south intrudes on an even older crater. Very high devastated walls overlaid with craters. Central mountain group and ridges.

RABBI LEVI. Crater 100 km in diameter. Walls of no great height and in a very ruined state. Numerous craters and hillocks in the interior.

STÖFLER. Very old enormous ring, 140 km across. Rounded walls encroached upon by Faraday. Deep crater on the inner slope to the south. Smooth floor crossed by rays from Tycho, and covered with many spots.

* * *

The distribution of the craters in this region is typical; it corresponds indeed to the laws of chance, which is the basis of the meteoric theory. The volcanic hypothesis does not find it easy to explain the intrusion of one crater on another.

110

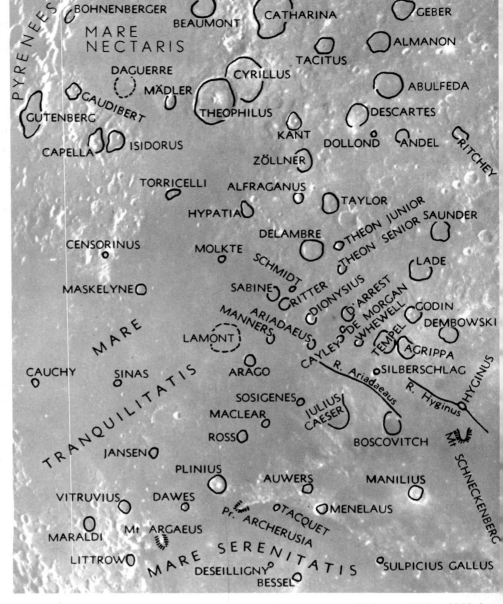

PLATE 9

FEATURES OF NOTE

ABULFEDA & ALMANON. Two mountain rings 60 and 45 km in diameter, between which extends a formation like a chain of craterlets. Possibly an old crevasse the walls of which have crumbled in many places due to effects of heat and the impact of small meteorites ; the powdered rock would have progressively filled the cleft, leaving the centres of the landslip still gaping, which would thus assume the appearance of craterlets.

CATHARINA. Very old walled plain 90 km in diameter. High walls, reaching 4800 m, very rounded and broken. Numerous craterlets on the floor and at the edges.

HYGINUS cleft 21 March 1945 — 2045 hrs — Photo 51.

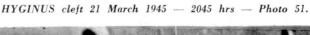

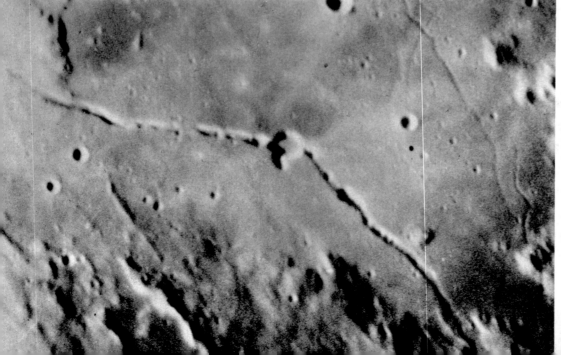

CYRILLUS. Crater 90 km across, of more recent formation than Catharina but intruded upon by Theophilus which is still younger. Central hill, craterlets, ridges and clefts.

HYGINUS CLEFT. Large fault, partially filled with material originating in neighbouring seas. The line of the cleft seems to have been made up of small craters which could have weakened the surface locally. Surrounding region strewn with other clefts and ridges.

JULIUS CAESAR. Very irregular formation with a gap in the west. Walls and floor considerably devastated and broken up.

THEOPHILUS. Great ringed plain more than 100 km in diameter. Prototype of a young formation characterised by sharp edges and an unbroken wall, which here rises 5000 m above the floor. Broad inner slope intersected by terraces. Very large central mountain group.

112

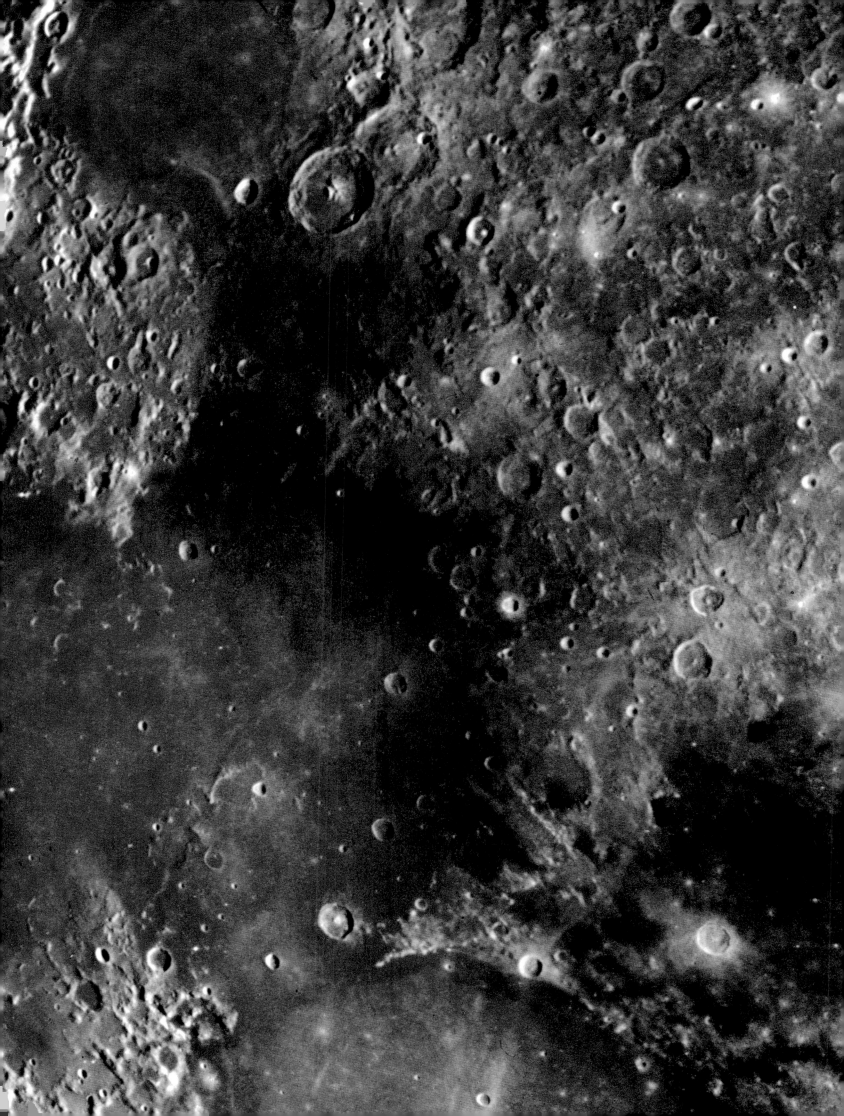

PLATE 10

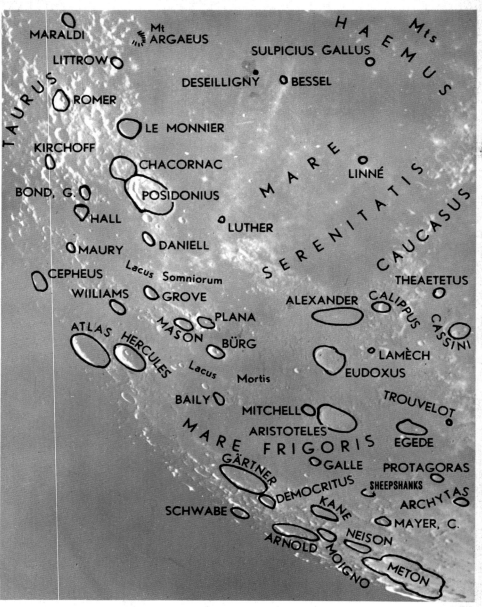

14 January 1944 — 18.06 days.

FEATURES OF NOTE

ALEXANDER. Very old ring 100 km across, having suffered considerably from erosion. Walls of low altitude.

ARISTOTELES. Large walled plain 100 km in diameter. Terraced walls, from which rise up peaks of 3500 m. Hillocks and traces of rings in the floor.

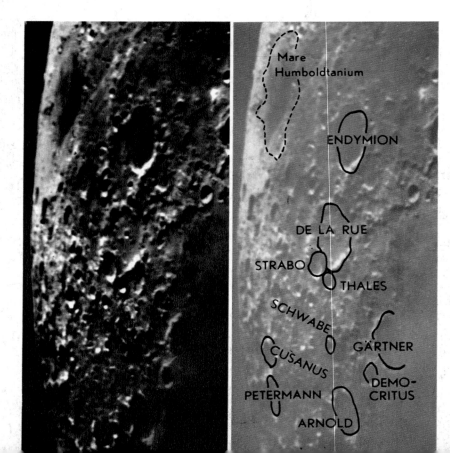

ATLAS. Great crater 85 km across. Inner slope intersected by terraces. High wall, especially in the north : from 2700 to 3300 m. Remains of old craters, hillocks, craterlets and clefts in the floor.

EUDOXUS. Crater 65 km in diameter. Walls rising to 3300 m in the west but little to the east.

GÄRTNER. A very old large formation much reduced by erosion. Walls almost non-existent on the south side but still well marked on the north.

HERCULES. Crater 75 km in diameter, forming with its neighbour Atlas a striking pair. Slope intersected with terraces, and walls reaching some 3000 m.

LINNÉ. Craterlet 900 m in diameter with a wall 30 m high. Very variable in appearance according to the illumination. Renowned for its « changes ».

MARE SERENITATIS. Huge circular area nearly 700 km in diameter. Strewn with ridges, one of which winds from north to south in its western region and in places rises to 200 m.

114

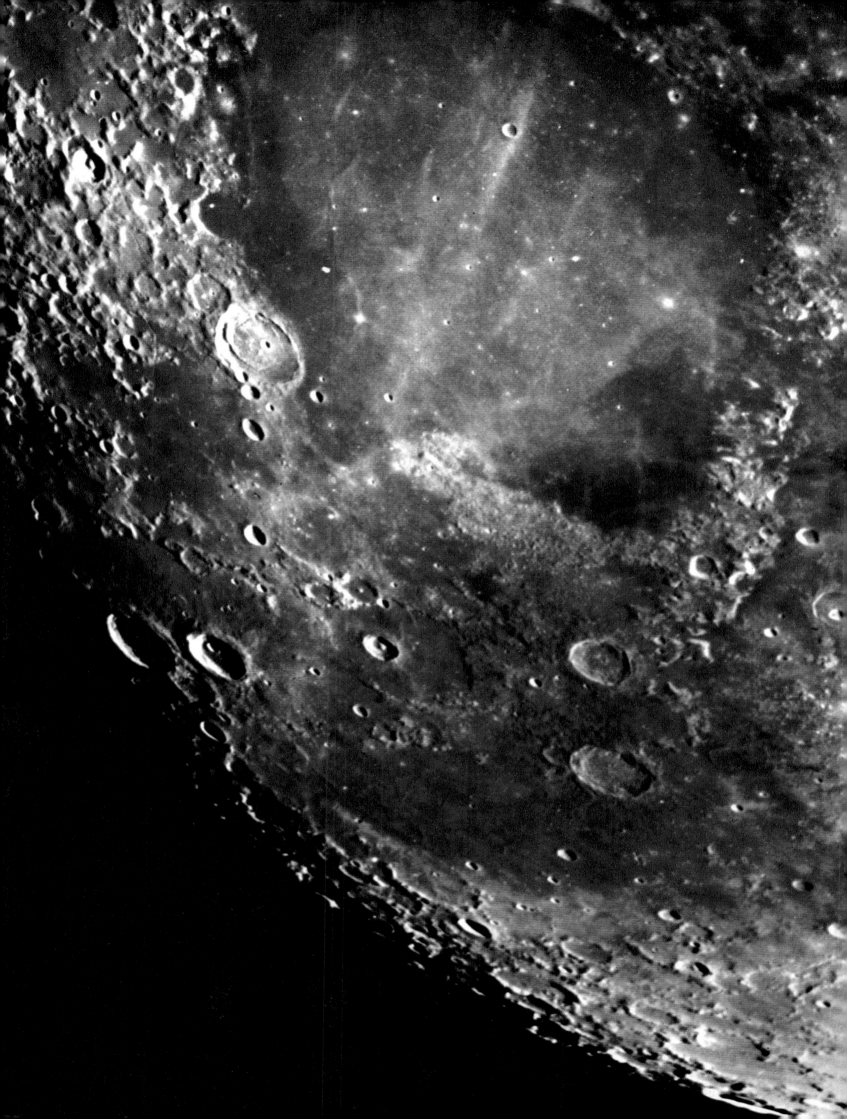

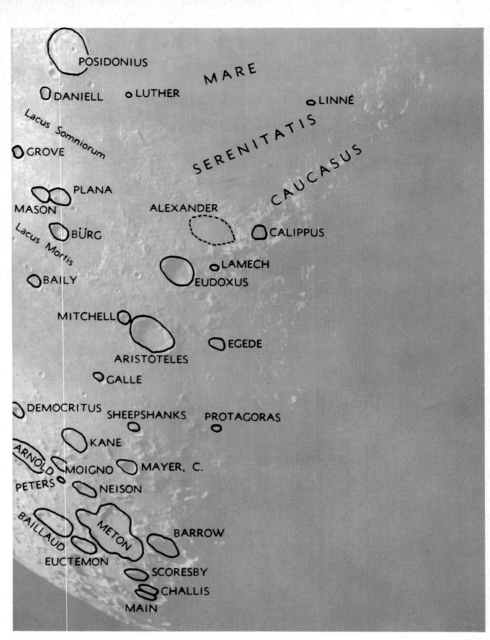

2 January 1944 — 6.62 days.

PLATE 11

FEATURES OF NOTE

BAILLAUD. Very large old ring ; the floor and walls overlapped by numerous craters.

POSIDONIUS 20 February 1961 — Photo 52.

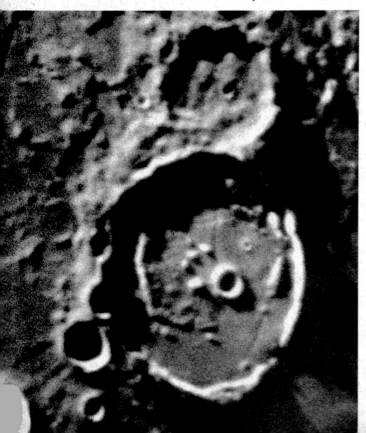

BARROW. Old crater 70 km in diameter. Walls extremely broken. Craters on the edges and on the floor.

CAUCASUS. Mountain chain situated between the Mare Imbrium and the Mare Serenitatis. Extremely high peaks, the highest summit reaching some 6000 m.

CHALLIS & MAIN. Two craters of similar dimensions, about 50 km in diameter. The second, broken into by the first, pretty well marks the lunar north pole.

METON. Very large formation exceeding 160 km in extent, formed by several craters close together. The floor is grey, relatively smooth, containing some craterlets, clefts and ridges.

PLANA. Old crater about 30 km in diameter. Rather low walls, broken up and even completely missing in places.

POSIDONIUS. Vast ringed plain 100 km in diameter. Particularly contorted structure of the interior which is crossed by multiple broken clefts. Apparent break in the floor which seems to have been partly raised up. In the interior, hills, traces of an old ring as well as an almost central crater and some craterlets. Narrow walls of no great height, not exceeding 1800 m.

SCORESBY. Deep crater 55 km in diameter. Terraced walls. Twin central peak.

116

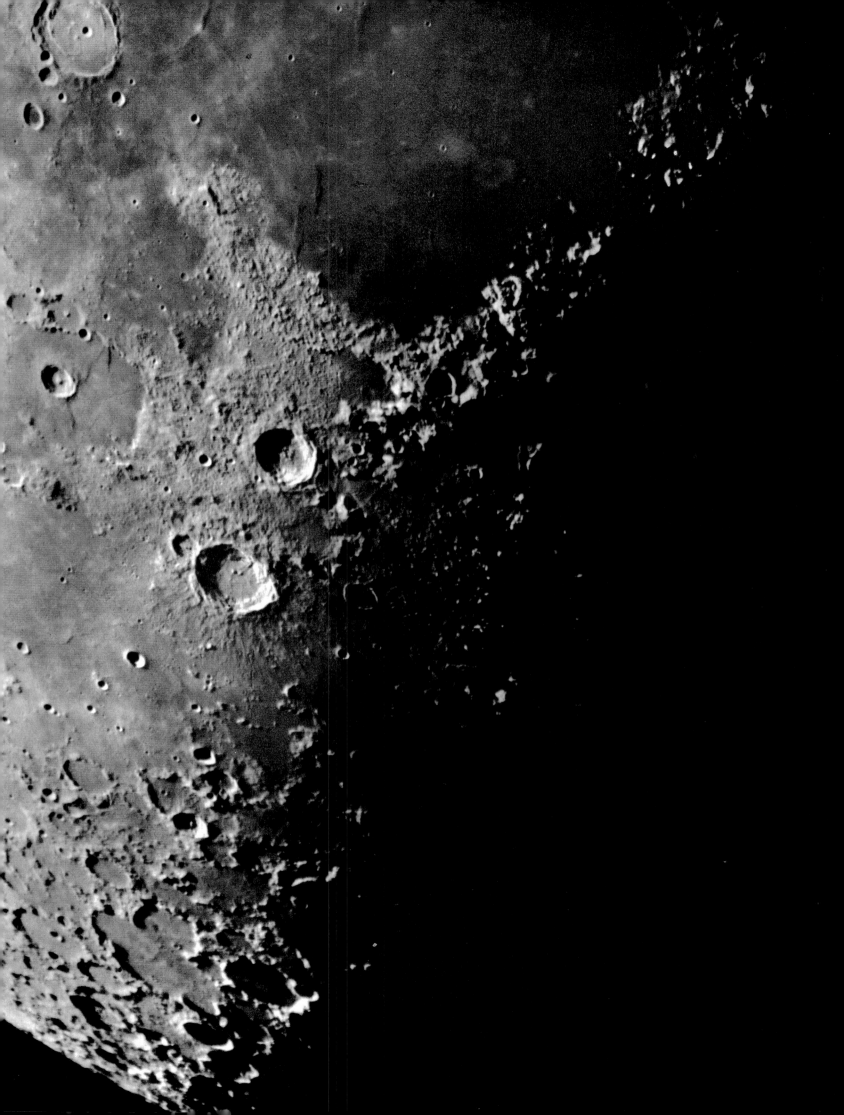

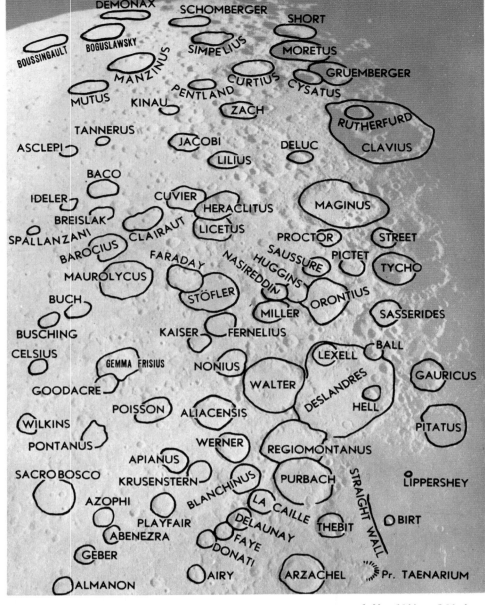

1 May 1944 — 8.94 days.

PLATE 12

FEATURES OF NOTE

ABENEZRA & AZOPHI. Twin craters 40 km in diameter. The first, the younger, has higher walls (4500 m and 3300 m respectively) and it intrudes slightly on its companion.

BOGUSLAWSKY. Crater almost 100 km in diameter. Terraced walls, from which high peaks rise to 3400 m. Hillocks and a crater on the floor.

DEMONAX. Crater 115 km across. Almost unbroken wall. Floor covered with craters and crossed by several ridges.

DESLANDRES. Immense area extending over nearly 200 km merely comprising the remains of a very old ring on which are superimposed Lexell and Ball to the south, and Hell on the east. Strewn with craters, hillocks and clefts.

GEMMA FRISIUS. Old ring formation 130 km in diameter. Very ruined walls on which Goodacre intrudes. Craters, craterlets, ridges and hillocks on the floor and the inner slopes.

LA CAILLE. Very regular crater 50 km in diameter. High walls particularly in the west. Hillocks and craterlets in the interior.

MILLER. Ringed plain 50 km in diameter, wall encroached upon by Nasireddin. Central mountain group and numerous craterlets on the floor and edges.

ORONTIUS, HUGGINS & NASIREDDIN. Group of three craters showing clearly the order of their formation. Orontius, the oldest and largest, riddled with craterlets, is the most irregular in shape. The west wall is intruded upon by Huggins, with a diameter of 65 km, and itself partly broken up by Nasireddin. Diameter of the latter : 50 km.

PURBACH. Great walled plain 120 km in diameter. Walls rising to 2400 m. North wall destroyed by a newer crater. Floor strewn with craterlets and ridges.

REGIOMONTANUS. Large ringed formation of the same type as its neighbour Purbach but with slightly larger dimensions. Irregular walls reaching 2000 m. Floor containing numerous craterlets and the remains of a central mountain group.

SACROBOSCO. Ring 85 km in diameter of irregular shape. Very high broad wall, 3500 m high, but showing gaps in places.

SAUSSURE. Crater 50 km in diameter. Terraced walls to the east rising to 2400 m.

WALTER. Great walled plain 150 km in diameter intruding slightly on Deslandres. Massive wall with summits reaching 3500 m. In the interior, numerous craters, ridges and hillocks.

SACROBOSCO · KRUSENSTERN · PLAYFAIR · BLANCHINUS · PURBACH · STRAIGHT WALL · LIPPERSHEY · LA CAILLE · AZOPHI · DELAUNAY · THEBIT · BIRT · ABENEZRA · FAYE · GEBER · DONATI · ARZACHEL · Pr. TAENARIUM · ALMANON · AIRY · ARGELANDER · ALPETRAGIUS · VOGEL · PARROT · LASSELL · ABULFEDA · BURNHAM · ALPHONSUS · DESCARTES · RITCHEY · KLEIN · DAVY · DOLLOND · ANDEL · ALBATEGNIUS · PTOLEMAEUS · PALISA · HALLEY · MÜLLER · HIND · HIPPARCHUS · GYLDEN · HERSCHEL · TAYLOR · SAUNDER · HORROCKS · SPÖRER · LALANDE · THEON JUNIOR · PICKERING, E · SEELIGER · REAUMUR · FLAMMARION · THEON SENIOR · LADE · OPPOLZER · MÖSTING · RHAETICUS · SÖMMERING · DE MORGAN · D'ARREST · GODIN · DEMBOWSKI · BLAGG · BRUCE · SCHRÖTER · TEMPEL · AGRIPPA · Sinus Medii · CHLADNI · CAYLEY · WHEWELL · SILBERSCHLAG · TRIESNECKER · MURCHISON · PALLAS · R. Hyginus · HYGINUS · UCKERT · BODE · IULIUS CAESAR · R. Ariadaeus · OSOSIGENES · Mt SCHNECKENBERG · Sinus Aestuum · STADIUS · BOSCOVICH · AUWERS · MANILIUS · MARE VAPORUM · ERATOSTHENES · MENELAUS

1 May 1944 — 8.94 days.

PLATE 13

FEATURES OF NOTE

ALBATEGNIUS. Walled plain 120 km in diameter. Broad wall with terraces, crowned by peaks reaching 3000 and 4000 m. Central hill. Overlapped by Klein.

FLAMMARION. Large ring of very irregular shape. Walls broken down and discontinuous. Numerous craterlets on the floor as well as several clefts.

HIPPARCHUS. Vast ringed formation 155 km in diameter. Very old and in a ruined condition. Walls only rise to 1200 m. Overlapped by Horrocks, a crater 30 km across.

PARROT. Irregular crater 60 km in diameter. Walls reach 1500 m.

PTOLEMAEUS. Very large old walled plain 140 km in diameter, situated almost at the centre of the lunar disc. Walls riddled with craterlets, rounded and discontinuous, from which rise peaks reaching 3000 m. Centre of crater filled with dark rather smooth material, suggesting a flow of liquid arrested by solidification ; the lava having originated in the interior of the Moon, or even from the melting of the surface as a result of the impact produced by the meteorite responsible for the crater. On the floor, a relatively recent crater 6.5 km in diameter, and several hundred craterlets of diameters less than a few hundred metres.

VOGEL. Curious elongated formation, formed by the fusion of three contiguous craters in a line. Central hill in the middle crater and central hillock in northern crater.

PTOLEMAEUS 21 March 1945 — Photo 53.

120

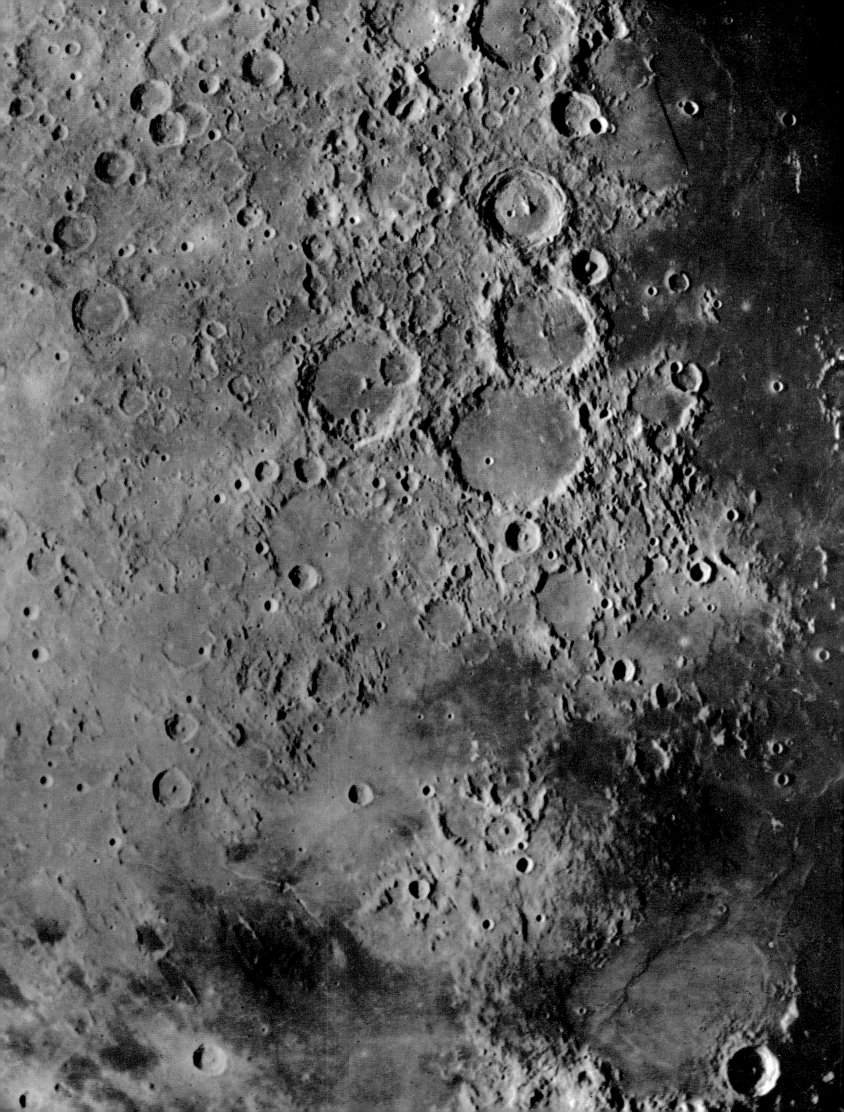

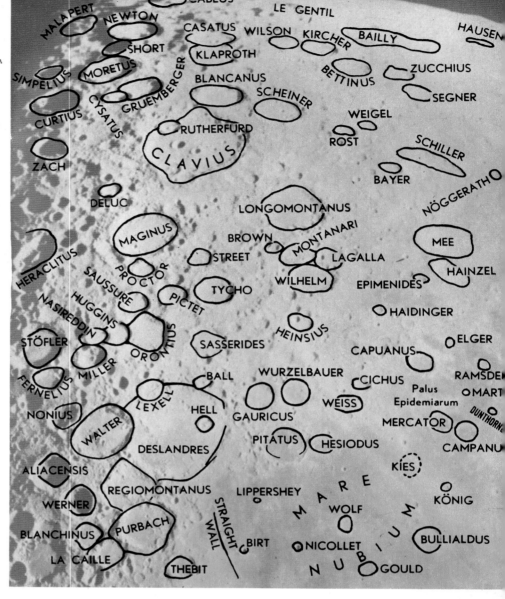

17 January 1944 — 21.06 days.

PLATE 14

FEATURES OF NOTE

BAILLY. The most extensive walled plain on the Moon reaching 290 km in diameter. Very high wall going up to a height of 4000 m. Hillocks, craterlets and ridges in the interior. Alternately visible and hidden as a consequence of libration.

BLANCANUS. A walled plain 100 km in diameter. Walls reaching 3500 m. Central peak.

CLAVIUS. One of the really enormous lunar formations. A very old ring 220 km in diameter. Broken walls, breached in many places, bristling with peaks rising to 5000 m. Several craters on the floor, the most important Rutherfurd having a diameter of 40 km. Numerous craterlets, ridges and hillocks, but no clefts.

KLAPROTH. Ring 100 km in diameter, with its southern wall broken into by Casatus.

LEIBNITZ MOUNTAINS. The highest mountain range on the Moon, extending over a very long distance. Heights of the peaks vary between 5000 and 8000 m, one even reaching 9000 m. Situated near the limb, they are periodically silhouetted in a remarkable fashion against the night sky.

LONGOMONTANUS. Enormous old ring 150 km in diameter. Walls strewn with peaks, but in ruined state and pitted with craters. Hills and craters in the interior.

MAGINUS. Immense old ring 175 km in diameter. High wall, 4000 m, broken up by numerous craters.

MALAPERT. Irregular ring formation 50 km across, surrounded by high walls ; very close to the lunar south pole.

NEWTON. The deepest crater, diameter 100 km. Composed of several craters close together.

PITATUS. Old formation 80 km across, badly damaged by erosion.

SCHEINER. Crater 110 km in diameter. Wall 5000 m high intersected by terraces.

TYCHO. One of the most striking features of the Moon. Not particularly obvious during half the lunation in the middle of an extraordinary chaotic region, it becomes absolutely stupendous during full Moon, outshining practically all nearby formations, so striking is its ray system. The rays issuing from its crater cover the surrounding region with their brilliance and some extend over half the lunar disc. A young crater 80 km in diameter, very regular in shape. Walls rising to 3500 m above the floor with a central peak 1500 m high.

WILHELM. Ring 100 km in diameter. High wall, 3500 m, pitted by some craters. On the floor, craters and craterlets, together with the traces of old ring formations. With Tycho, Maginus, Clavius and Longomontanus it forms an easy reference point in the shape of a pentagon at periods other than full Moon.

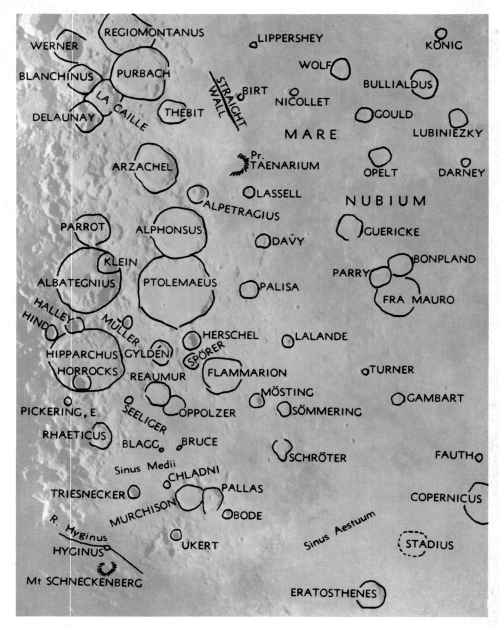

17 January 1944 — 21.06 days.

PLATE 15

FEATURES OF NOTE

ALPETRAGIUS. Crater some 40 km in diameter. Terraced walls 3500 m high. Central mountain with two summit craterlets.

ALPHONSUS. Crater 110 km in diameter. Very broad complex wall rising to 2000 m. Contorted floor with a tangled mass of crevasses, ridges and craters. Central mountain group. A puff of gas near the central peak was observed spectroscopically in November 1958 by Kozyrev, which would indicate the presence of volcanic activity on the Moon.

ALPHONSUS 21 March 1945 — Photo 54.

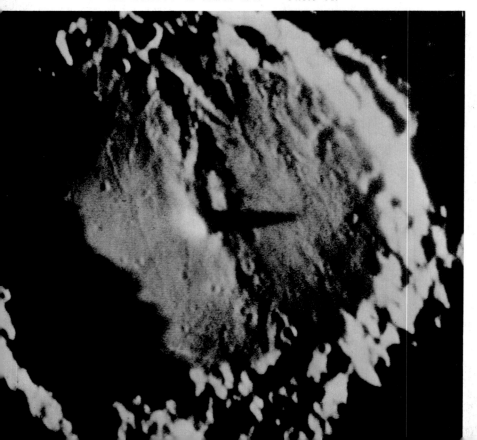

ARZACHEL. Crater 100 km in diameter. Wall from 3000 to 4000 m. Floor 1000 m above the surrounding surface with a central mountain 1500 m high. Craterlets and cracks.

BODE. Crater 18 km across and 1500 m deep. Particularly visible at full Moon.

HERSCHEL. Crater 45 km in diameter. Central mountain group with craterlet.

MÖSTING. Deep crater. Walls rising to 500 m above the land on outer side, but 2000 m above the floor. Central hillock. The small neighbouring crater, Mösting A, is used as a point of reference for observation of the Moon by the meridian telescope and has facilitated the determination of the motions of the Moon as well as, to a certain extent, the shape of the surface.

MURCHISON & PALLAS. Two rings 50 and 40 km in diameter, much worn down by erosion. Breached walls. Central hillock on Pallas.

SCHRÖTER. A very old and much eroded formation 30 km in diameter. Low wall with the south section completely missing.

THEBIT. Crater 50 km across. North wall overlapped by another crater 18 km in diameter.

124

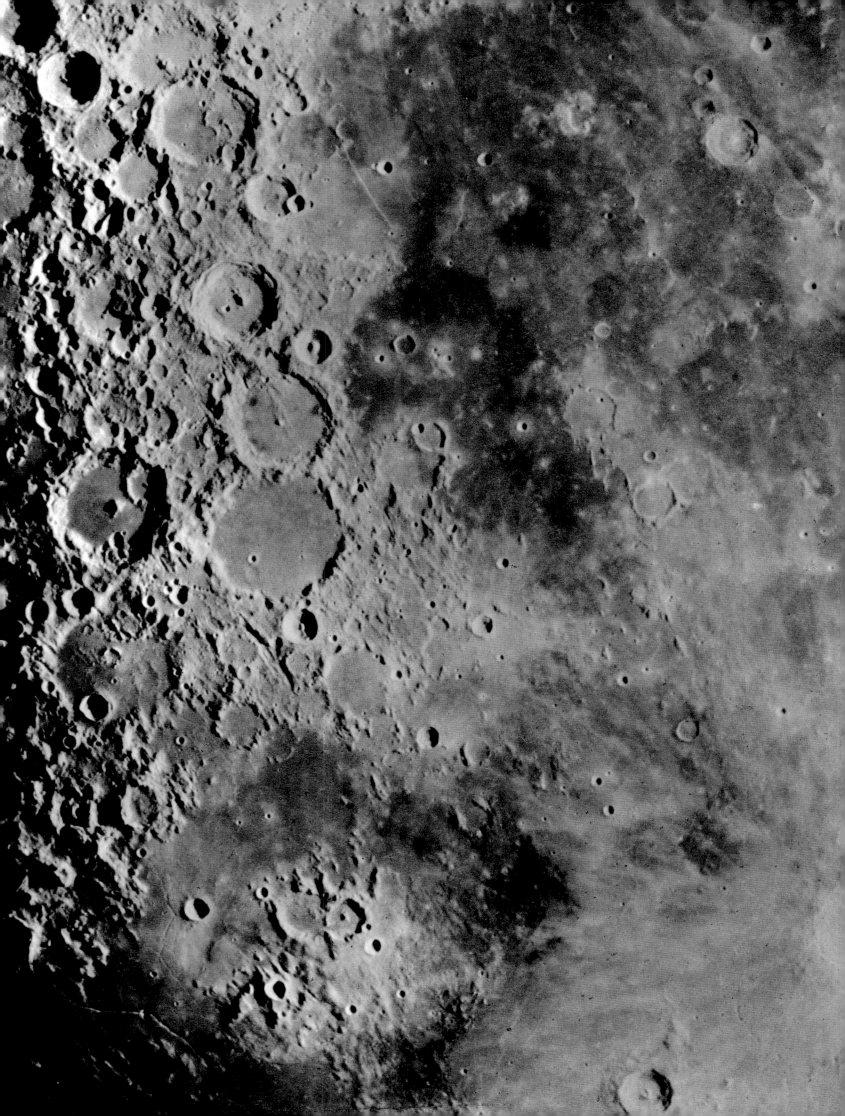

PLATE 16

FEATURES OF NOTE

APENNINES. Mountain range on the south-west border of the Mare Imbrium. Many high peaks : Wolff 3500 m ; Ampère 3000 m ; Huygens 5500 m ; and Hadley 4800 m.

CARPATHIANS. Discontinuous mountain range of low altitude. Peaks of 1500 and 2000 m.

COPERNICUS. Crater 90 km in diameter, one of the youngest lunar formations, characterized by the sharpness of its arêtes and its remarkable system of rays which extend in every direction. At full Moon, the bright circle surrounding the crater is even more brilliant than the rays.

31 May 1944 — 9.55 days.

Gentle slopes with terraces. Wall 3500 m above the surface of the floor. Central mountain group bristling with peaks.

ERATOSTHENES. Regularly shaped crater 60 km in diameter. Walls rising to almost 5000 m above the floor, which is itself 2500 m below the level outside the crater. Central mountain group.

STADIUS. Very old ring 60 km in diameter, of which only the outline remains, just visible in the dust. Riddled with craterlets of very small dimensions.

TIMOCHARIS. Very regular crater 40 km in diameter, isolated on the Mare Imbrium. Very fine but complex terraces.

TRIESNECKER 21 March 1945 — Photo 55.

Walls 2000 m above the floor. Outer slopes covered with numerous though slight radiating lines.

TRIESNECKER. Crater 23 km across, associated with a system of clefts and fissures, the most important being 1 to 3 km wide. Angular outline and intersection of clefts suggest a seismic origin.

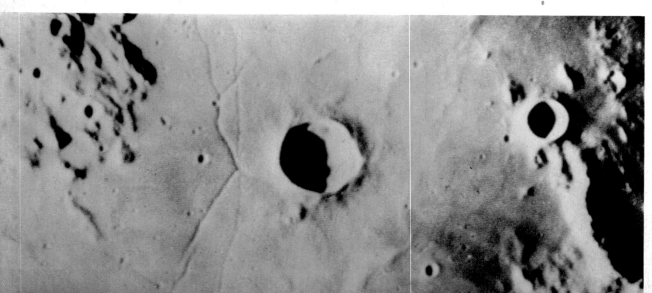

126

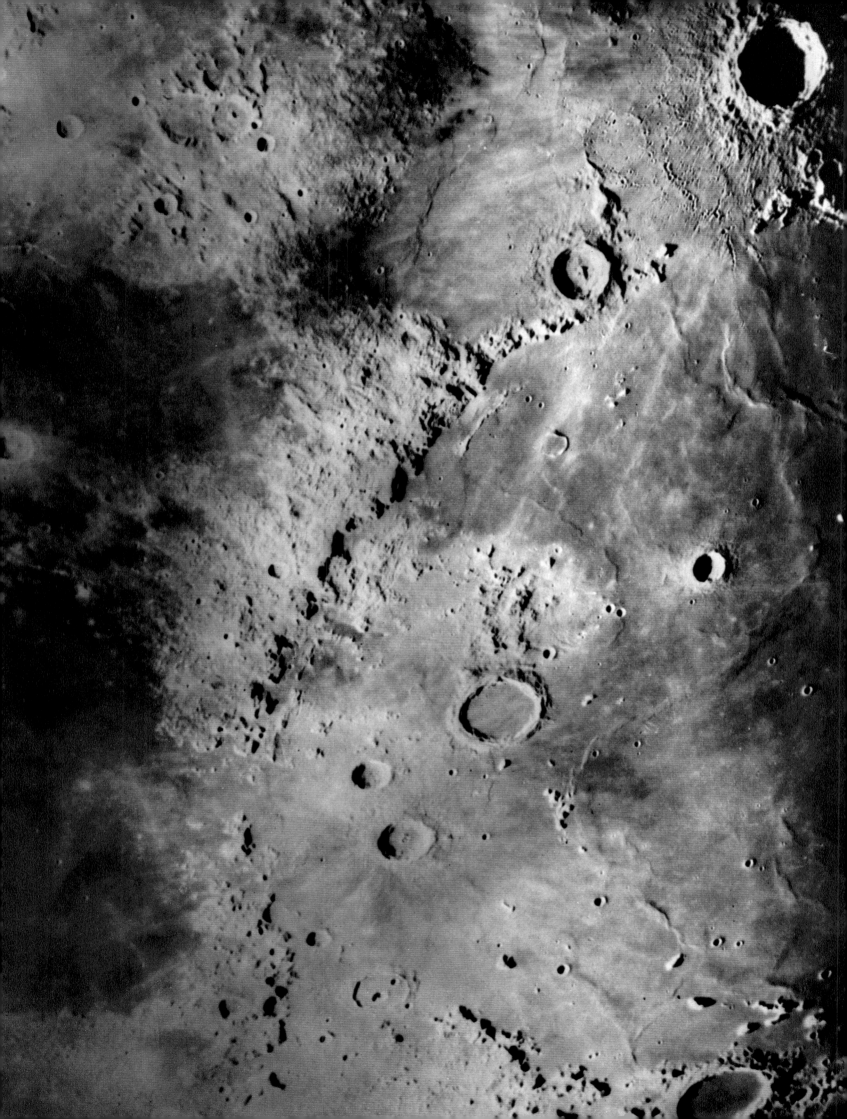

PLATE 17

FEATURES OF NOTE

ALPS. Mountain range bordering the Mare Imbrium in the north. Relatively high peaks, the highest, Mont Blanc, reaching about 4000 m.

ALPINE VALLEY. Gorge 130 km long in a straight line.

ARCHIMEDES. Huge ringed plain almost 100 km in diameter. Astonishingly smooth floor, shallow compared with the surrounding terrain, filled with the same material as the « seas » and divided into zones by east-west rays. Thick wall 1300 m high, crowned by peaks reaching 2000 m.

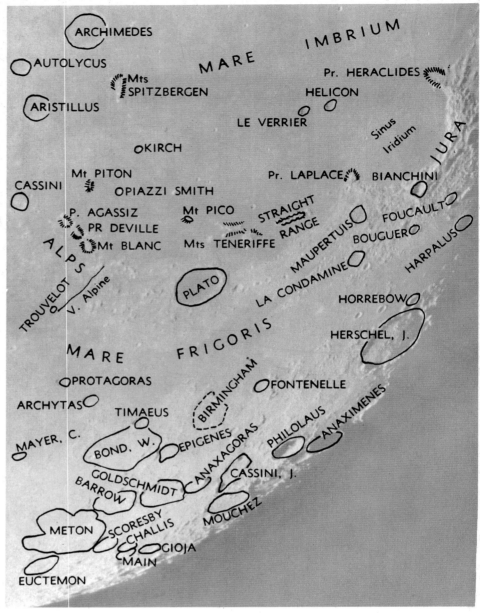

6 January 1944 — 10.70 days.

ARISTILLUS 21 March 1945 — Photo 56.

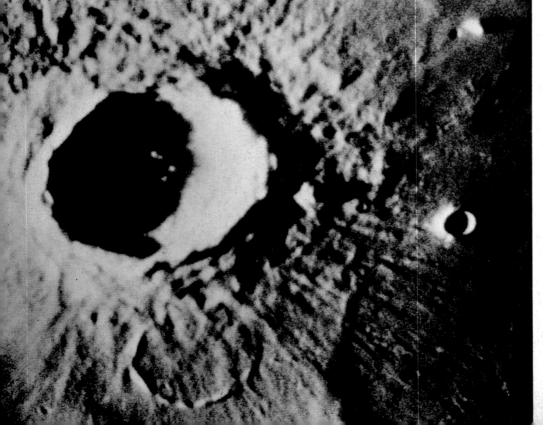

ARISTILLUS. Crater 55 km in diameter, showing the characteristics of recent formation : sharp ridges, well-defined terraces and traces of the explosion of the meteorite which caused the crater, i.e. radial grooves showing a furrowing of the surface. Walls 3000 m high. Central mountain group.

AUTOLYCUS. Crater 40 km in diameter. Terraced wall, with gaps in places, rising to 3000 m above the crater bottom.

PICO & PITON. Two isolated mountains about 2300 m high ; considered to be scattered fragments ejected as a result of the great meteoritic explosion which engendered the Mare Imbrium.

PLATO. Walled plain 100 km in diameter. Wall of jagged ridges ; 1000 m high with peaks reaching 2000 m. Smooth floor, formed of the same material as the « seas », but even darker. Some craterlets and numerous bright spots.

128

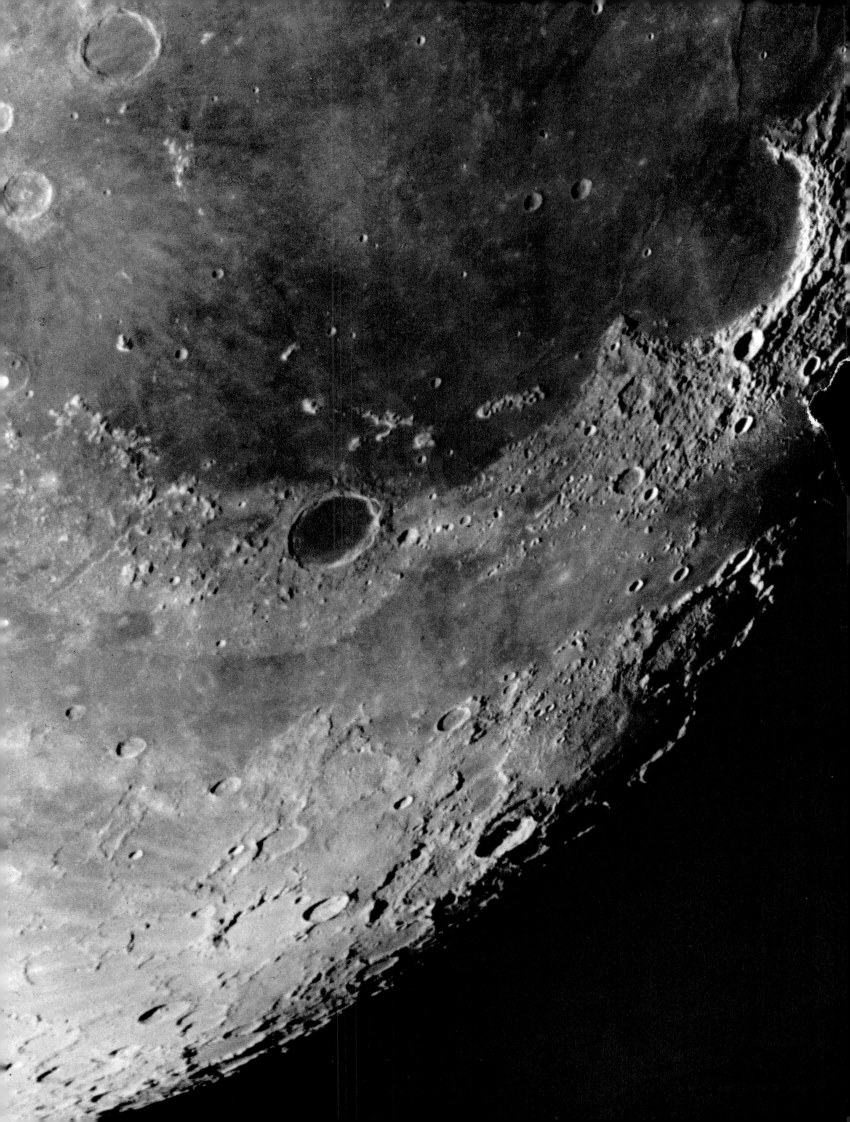

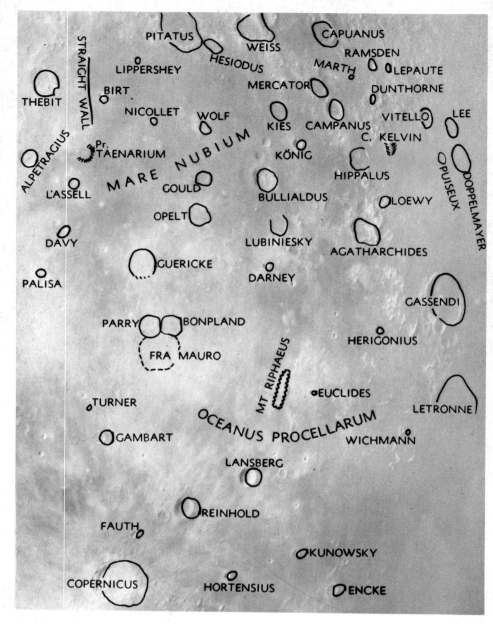

6 January 1944 — 10.70 days.

PLATE 18

FEATURES OF NOTE

BIRT. Small, very deep crater with walls rising 2000 m above the floor.

BONPLAND, FRA MAURO & PARRY. Group of three very old craters, rather large in size, very disintegrated and eroded. Walls of no great height and very damaged. Floors strewn with craters and broken fragments.

BULLIALDUS. Walled plain some 60 km in diameter. Massive walls rising 2400 m above the floor and intersected by terraces. Central mountain with the highest peak reaching 1000 m.

HORTENSIUS 29 April 1958 — Photo 57.

GUERICKE. Old ring formation 50 km in diameter. Wall largely open to the south and west. On the floor : craterlets, ridges and broken fragments.

HORTENSIUS. Crater 16 km across, quite deep, around which is found a certain number of hillocks possessing a small central pitformations considered as the remains of important volcanoes.

LANSBERG. Crater 47 km in diameter. High wall 3000 m above the floor. Central mountain crowned with peaks.

STRAIGHT WALL. Enormous cliff resulting from a fault ; 120 km long and dropping 500 m. Covered like the rest of the lunar surface with powdery substance.

REINHOLD. Crater 50 km in diameter. High wall, 3000 m. Central mountain group.

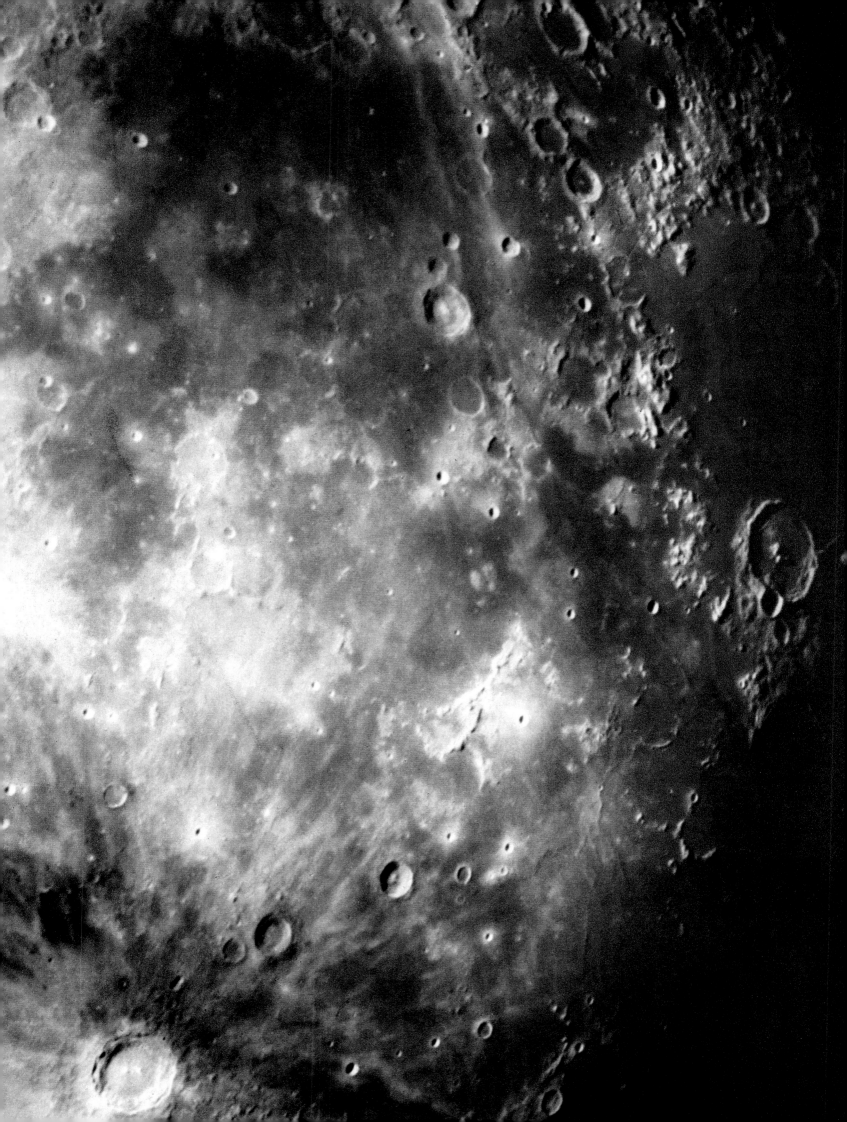

PLATE 19

FEATURES OF NOTE

CAPUANUS. Crater 50 km across, the floor of which is somewhat higher than the surrounding land. Large wall reaching 2400 m.

INGHIRAMI 25 August 1942 — Photo 58.

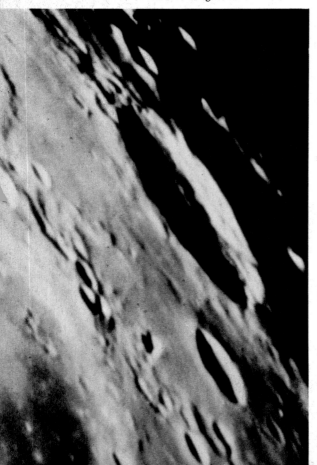

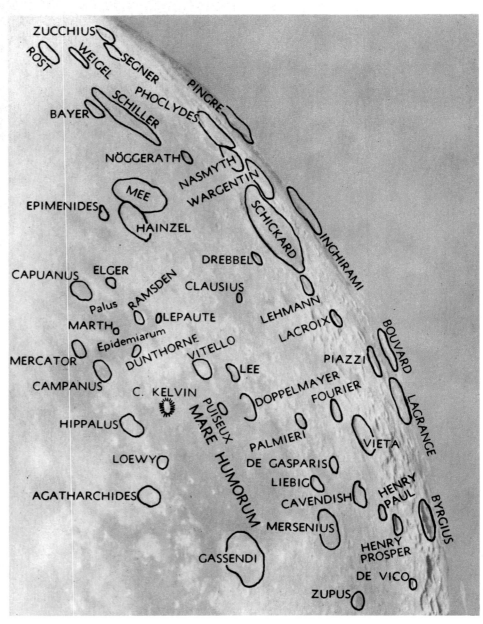

8 January 1944 — 12.79 days.

DOPPELMAYER. Walled plain 60 km in diameter, much eroded. Walls considerably worn away, especially on the northern side. Central mountain group 750 m high, divided into two sections.

HAINZEL. Extremely irregular formation, measuring 100 km across at a maximum. Probably a result of the fusion of two neighbouring craters. Walls 3000 m high covered with tiny craters.

INGHIRAMI. Vast crater 100 km in diameter, very near the limb and in consequence alternately hidden and visible. Walls 3700 m high. Small central mountain group.

SCHICKARD. Enormous ring formation 200 km in diameter. Walls only 1300 m high but topped by some high peaks rising to 3000 m. On the floor, a number of craters and some clefts.

SCHILLER. An elongated formation, 100 km by 180 km. Very likely formed by the fusion of two craters.

WARGENTIN. Crater 90 km in diameter, of an exceptional type, being the object of various hypotheses about its source and the origin of lunar formations in general. Inner surface elevated 300 m above the outer, showing that the liquid lava originally reached such a level that it overflowed and invaded the neighbouring crater.

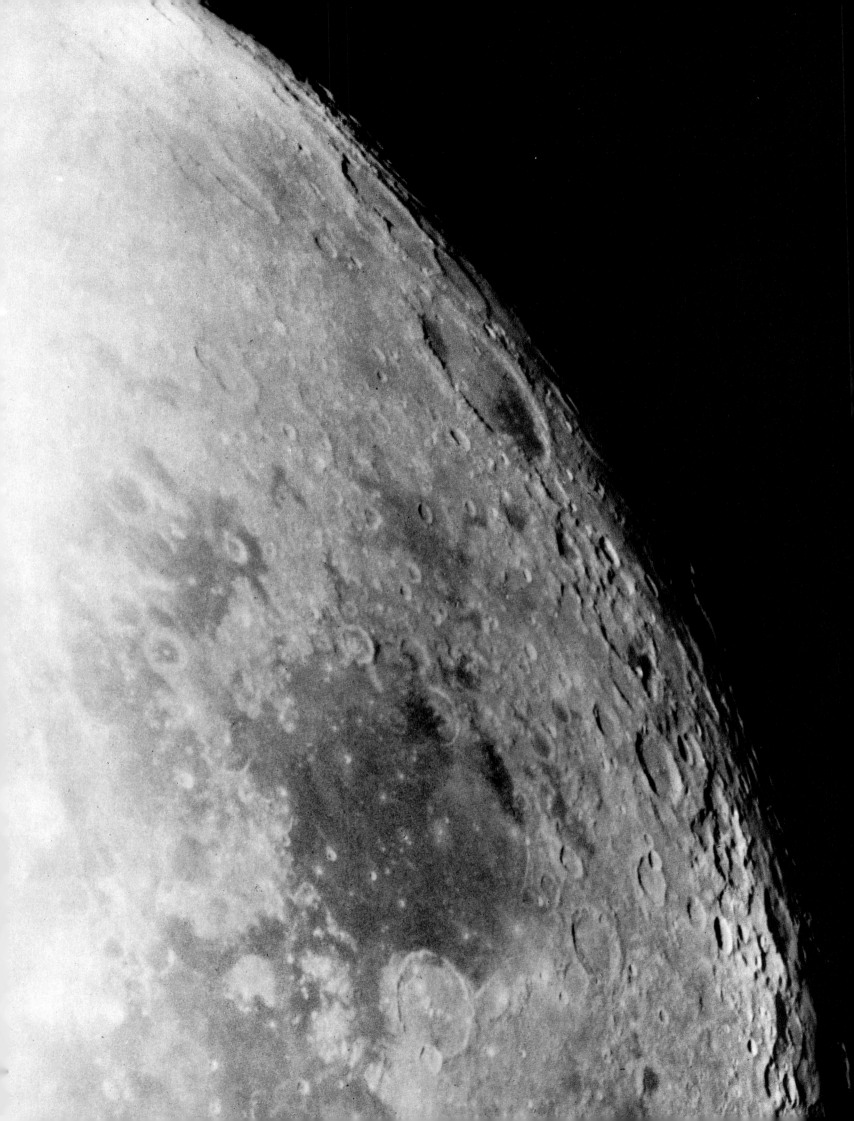

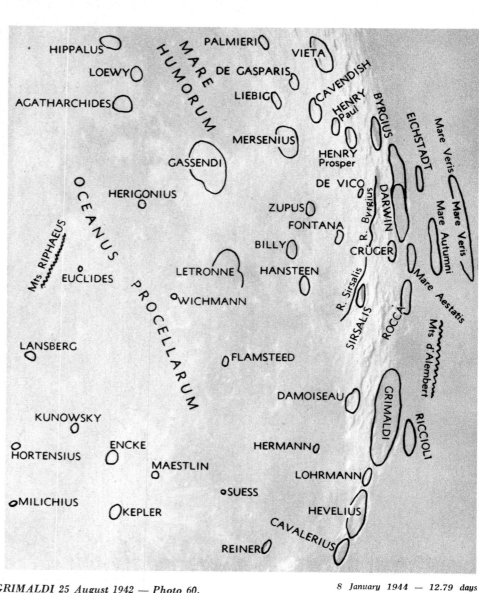

PLATE 20

FEATURES OF NOTE

BYRGIUS. Crater 65 km across. Situated very near the limb in the libration zone. Wall rising to 2000 m.

BYRGIUS cleft 25 August 1942 — Ph. 59.

GRIMALDI 25 August 1942 — Photo 60.

8 January 1944 — 12.79 days

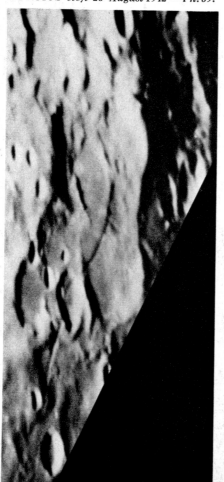

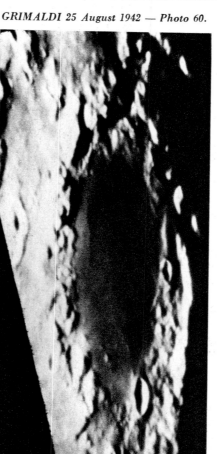

BYRGIUS CLEFT. Typical cleft crossing a variety of topographic obstacles : a hill, the wall of a crater, its floor and the wall opposite, another hillock, etc.

GASSENDI. Enormous walled plain 80 km in diameter. Walls with peaks rising to 3000 m. Floor situated 600 m higher than the surrounding surface, covered with ridges and numerous clefts. Central mountain group 1200 m high.

GRIMALDI. Great walled plain 200 km in diameter. Broken wall reaching 1200 m high in places. Perfectly flat dark floor, suggesting that the molten lava had initially covered a larger surface on the northern edge and had later withdrawn from its original shore-line, causing the partly remolten undulations to reappear.

SIRSALIS CLEFT. The largest cleft on the Moon ; it is continued to the south by the Byrgius cleft with several branches.

134

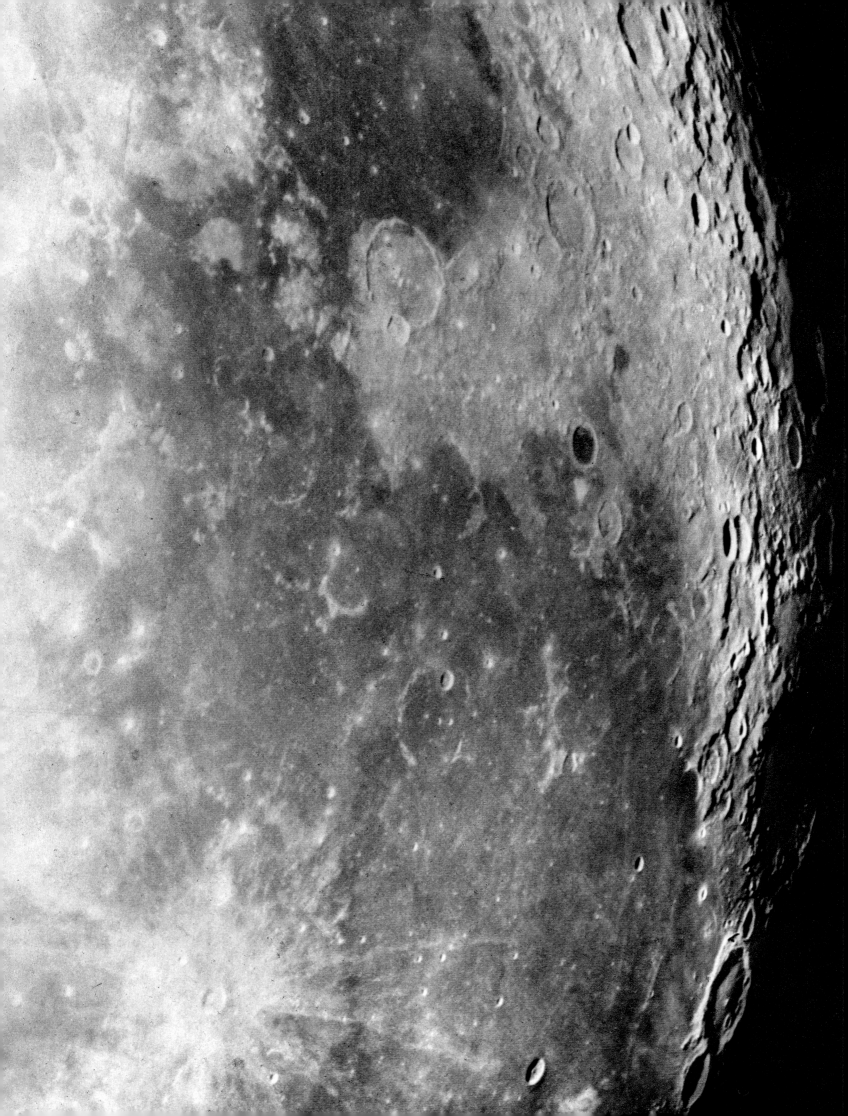

PLATE 21

LANSBERG
SUESS
HEVELIUS
CAVALERIUS
KUNOWSKY
MAESTLIN
REINER
OLBERS
ENCKE
O C E A N U S
HORTENSIUS
KEPLER
GALILAEI
CARDANUS
MARIUS
MILICHIUS
KRAFFT
VASCO DE GAMA
BESSARION
P R O C E L L A R U M
MAYER, T.
HERODOTUS
SELEUCUS
C. BANAT
SCHIAPARELLI
BRAYLEY
Mts Hercynian
DRAPER
ARISTARCHUS
STRUVE.
Mts HARBINGER
PRINZ
PYTHEAS
V. Schröter
BRIGGS
EULER
DIOPHANTUS
KRIEGER
LICHTENBERG
LAMBERT
WOLLASTON
DELISLE
ANGSTRÖM
ULUGH BEIGH
Mt LA HIRE
GRUITHUISEN
NAUMANN
HEIS
LAVOISIER
CARLINI
HERSCHEL, C.

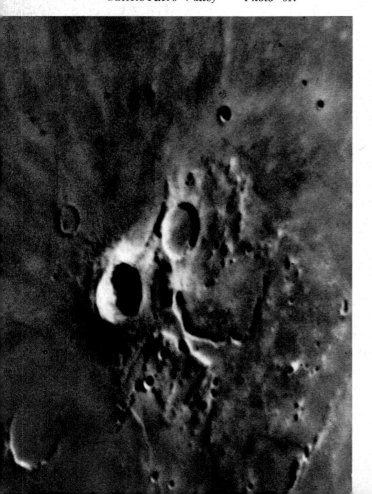

FEATURES OF NOTE

ARISTARCHUS. A young crater 45 km in diameter, the very brightly coloured floor of which shines with vivid intensity, particularly when it is full Moon. Rays extend especially to the south and south-west. Walls of low altitude, only reaching 650 m above the surrounding surface. Central mountain 300 m high.

HERODOTUS. Crater 37 km across, its dark floor in sharp contrast to that of its neighbour Aristarchus. Narrow wall rising to 1200 m.

KEPLER. Crater 35 km in diameter. Remarkable ray system with rays extending in all directions, crossing in the north-west those issuing from Aristarchus, and in the west those from Copernicus. Terraced wall with peaks rising to 3000 m.

SCHRÖTER'S VALLEY. Remarkable type of fault in the shape of a W, about 200 km long. One end touches the north wall of Herodotus; covered in a layer of debris resulting from the impact responsible for Aristarchus. Walls and floor covered with granular powder showing particularly well the way the material, disintegrated by the impact of small meteorites and by temperature variations, trickles into the cracks and slowly fills them up. Schröter's Valley is situated inside a lozenge-shaped mountain region, yellowish in colour and quite exceptional. The characteristic outline of this formation seems to indicate that it originated in the impact which formed the Mare Imbrium.

136

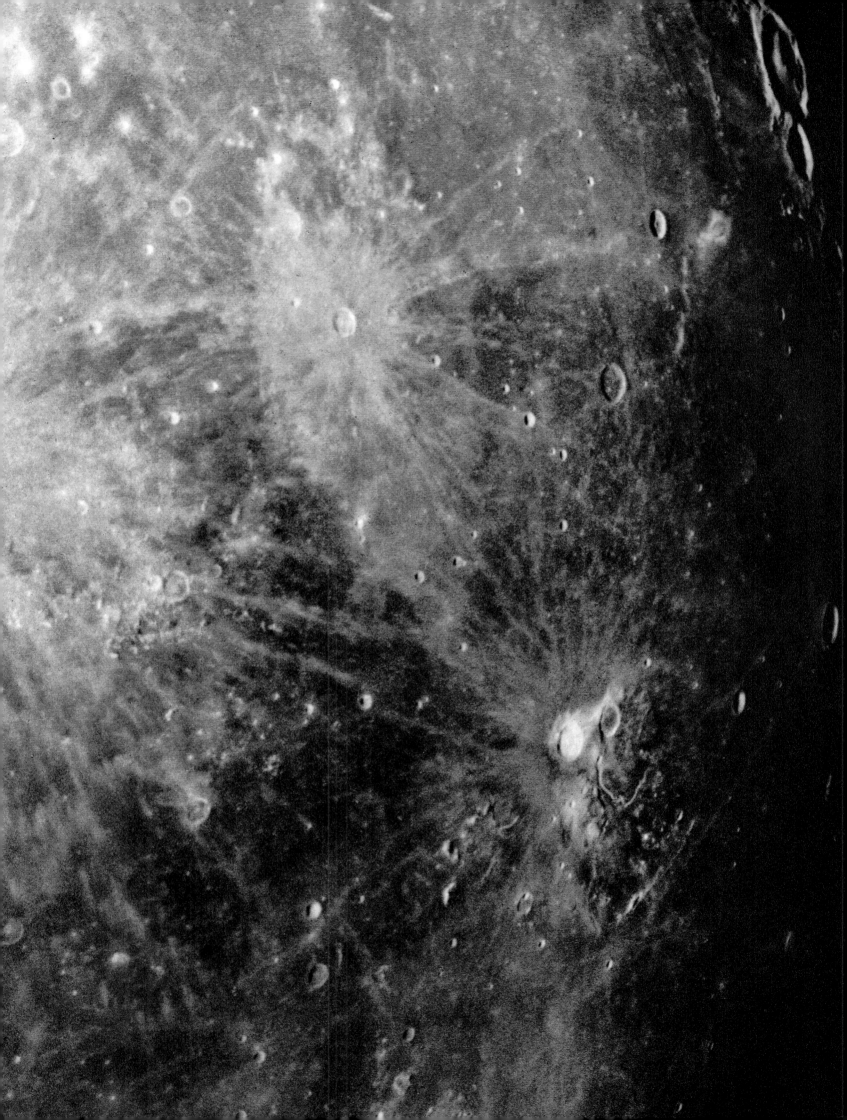

PLATE 22

FEATURES OF NOTE

HERSCHEL, J. Large area 150 km long, rather irregular, surrounded by walls generally of low altitude. Surface covered with hillocks, craters and ridges.

PYTHAGORAS. Great ring 120 km in diameter. Terraced walls reaching 5000 m. Central mountain group.

PYTHAGORAS 25 August 1942 — Photo 62.

SINUS IRIDUM. Semi-circular bay which could have been hollowed out by the impact of the meteorite which produced the Mare Imbrium. Surface level slowly falls from the Mare Imbrium to 600 m lower down. Bounded by the Jura mountains in the north-east, which contain peaks reaching 6000 m. Framed by the promontories of Heraclides and Laplace, with respective altitudes of 1200 and 2700 m.

STRAIGHT RANGE. Mountain range 65 km long, rather narrow and relatively low. Highest point 1800 m.

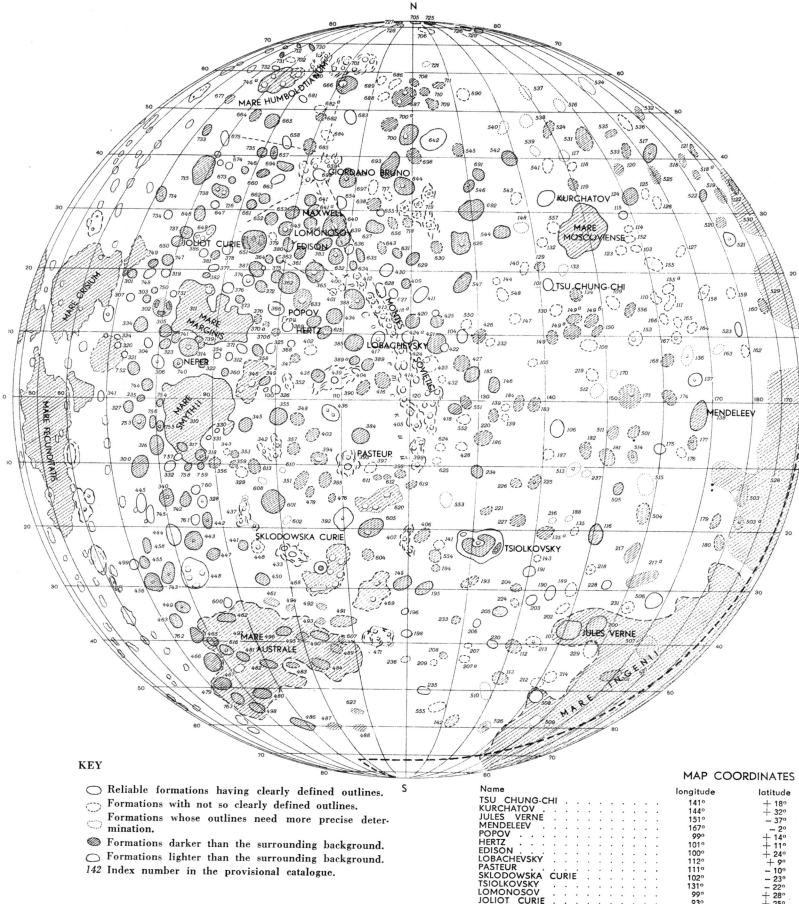

KEY

◯ Reliable formations having clearly defined outlines.

⬡ Formations with not so clearly defined outlines.

⬡ Formations whose outlines need more precise determination.

▨ Formations darker than the surrounding background.

◯ Formations lighter than the surrounding background.

142 Index number in the provisional catalogue.

THE OTHER FACE OF THE MOON. — *Map drawn up, between January and April 1960, from photographic documents transmitted by the automatic interplanetary station (Lunik III) on the 7 October 1959. In collaboration with the Institue of Scientific Studies, Geodesy and Cartography and the State Institute of Astronomy of the U.S.S.R.*

MAP COORDINATES

Name	longitude	latitude
TSU CHUNG-CHI	141°	+ 18°
KURCHATOV	144°	+ 32°
JULES VERNE	151°	− 37°
MENDELEEV	167°	− 2°
POPOV	99°	+ 14°
HERTZ	101°	+ 11°
EDISON	100°	+ 24°
LOBACHEVSKY	112°	+ 9°
PASTEUR	111°	− 10°
SKLODOWSKA CURIE	102°	− 23°
TSIOLKOVSKY	131°	− 22°
LOMONOSOV	99°	+ 28°
JOLIOT CURIE	93°	+ 25°
MAXWELL	99°	+ 30°
GIORDANO BRUNO	103°	+ 36°
MONTES SOVIETICI	from 111°	+ 19°
	to 124°	− 5°
MARE INGENII		
MARE MOSCOVIENSE	149°	+ 27°

This map has been reproduced from ATLAS OF THE UNKNOWN FACE OF THE MOON, Academy of Sciences, U.S.S.R., Moscow 1960. The names given to formations are those approved by the International Astronomical Union.

Part Three

ASTRONAUTICAL PRINCIPLES

The journey to the Moon

XVII

EXTRATERRESTRIAL
TRAJECTORIES

Few ambitions have given rise to more long and laborious studies than the conquest of the Moon. Since Newton's discovery of the law of universal gravitation, man has relentlessly sought the means of creating the tremendous speed required to set him free from the Earth. It has taken nearly 300 years to find a solution to this formidable problem, a solution which is, in theory, simple.

Circular Velocity

If the Earth were stripped of its atmosphere, a shell fired horizontally at increasing muzzle velocities would, as we have seen, finally turn indefinitely around it. The critical speed established in this way, which causes a projectile to take up a trajectory parallel to the ground, has been given the name of *circular velocity*. Of course it is an exclusively theoretical notion since the atmosphere is supposed to be non-existent ; its value can be deduced from the equilibrium which must exist between centrifugal force and gravity.

Circular velocity reaches its maximum value quite close to the Earth for it varies with gravity. An object fired at ground level and parallel to it must have a speed of 7.9 km/s in order to describe a circular orbit ; if the firing takes place at a height of 10,000 metres the aforementioned speed is reduced to 4.94 km/s, and at 384,000 kilometres from the centre of the Earth it only has a value of 1017 m/s which, as we know, is the orbital velocity of the Moon.

Strictly speaking, however, these figures are only exact if we consider the gun to be situated at one of the poles and to fire its projectile along the line of a meridian. If it is situated on the equator it undergoes the maximum influence of the motion of the Earth's rotation and the circular velocity is slightly different ; it also varies with the orientation of the gun. If fired towards the east the projectile benefits from the speed of the equatorial circumference, that is to say, by 465 m/s, and the circular velocity is reduced by this amount. On the other hand the speed is increased by this same half kilometre per second if the shell is fired towards the west.

The calculation which produces these varying values of circular speed provides us at the same time with the period of the corresponding revolution. At the surface of the Earth an artificial satellite would theoretically take 84 minutes to encircle the Earth. At a height of a thousand metres it would need 1 hour 45 minutes, and at the distance of the Moon the interval of time is, as we have seen, $27\frac{1}{4}$ days. It is also worth noting the case of a satellite launched towards the east in the equatorial plane and made to orbit at a height of 35,8000 kilometres, that is 42,200 kilometres from the centre of the Earth. Such a rocket would take exactly 24 hours to complete a full revolution so that it would appear to be absolutely still in the sky. In this respect it would be of considerable interest to numerous branches of science and particularly for telecommunications and geodesy. To astronomers it would offer exceptional conditions for the installation of an observatory.

Obviously the next question is to know what will happen if a speed greater than the orbital velocity is given to a projectile at the heights indicated in the previous paragraphs. The trajectory becomes an ellipse which the rocket follows in conformity with the laws of Kepler ; and as the centre of the Earth is the point at which the attraction is exerted, it forms one of the foci of the elliptical orbit. As the initial velocity increases the ellipse becomes more elongated, but the first focus always remains identical with the centre of the Earth so that it is the second which progressively moves further away until it is right out at infinity. The ellipse then becomes a parabola and the trajectory is no longer closed ; this means that the projectile moves away from the Earth for ever.

Parabolic and Hyperbolic Velocities

The muzzle velocity which causes the trajectory to be a parabola is 11.2 km/s at ground level ; this also decreases with height : at a height of 200 metres the value is 11 km/s, and at 1000 metres it is only 10.4 km/s. This is frequently called *escape velocity*, a term which no doubt conjures up the idea of a departure without return,

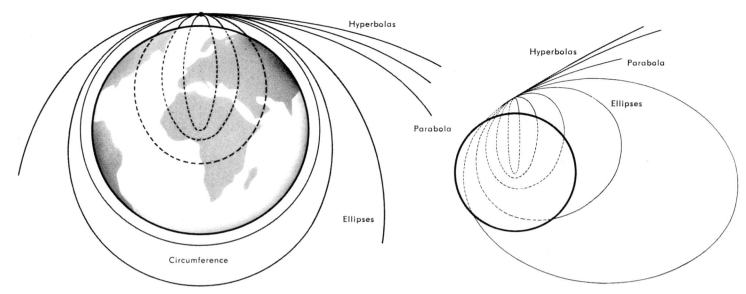

Fig. 53. — Theoretical paths of a shell fired horizontally. Due to air resistance, trajectories outside the Earth are not feasible if the gun is situated in the atmosphere. Note that for each launching point there are any number of elliptical and hyperbolic paths but only one which is a parabola.

Fig. 54. — Theoretical paths of a shell fired upwards. This diagram shows that it is not possible to create an artificial satellite if an attempt is made to achieve its orbital speed at the moment of leaving the Earth's surface. Either the trajectory is elliptical when the rocket will inescapably hit the ground or the trajectory is parabolic or hyperbolic in which case the rocket will never return.

but which is somewhat confusing since the circular velocity is already sufficient to keep the satellite away from the Earth indefinitely. Besides, this terminology suggests to some that a body travelling at escape velocity no longer undergoes the action of gravity or escapes the Earth's attraction. Now although the body may have effectively overcome it, its constant action is in no way diminished, even to infinity. Therefore the more precise expression *parabolic velocity* is to be preferred ; this expresses the phenomenon in a more accurate and scientific manner. Likewise, the expression *hyperbolic velocities* should be used to designate those which are still greater than parabolic velocity and which give rise to other trajectories, also non-closed, that are arcs of a hyperbola.

The following summary may be made of the conclusions drawn for different cases of the horizontal firing of a projectile (Fig. 53).

— If the initial speed is less than circular velocity, the trajectory is the arc of an ellipse ; this closed curve may be produced inside the Earth, the most distant focus from the gun being the centre of the Earth. This forms the usual case for artillery shells which fall back to the surface of the Earth, no account being taken here of the air resistance.

— If the initial speed is equal to circular velocity, the trajectory is a circle. Here we have the particular case where the two foci of the ellipse are identical ; the projectile never touches the ground again.

— If the initial speed is greater than circular velocity, but lower than parabolic velocity, the trajectory remains elliptical but the centre of the Earth now forms the closest focus to the gun. The projectile turns around the Earth, its distance from the surface varying continually ; the greater the initial velocity, the more distant the point of apogee.

— If the initial speed is equal to parabolic velocity, the trajectory causes the projectile to move away from the terrestrial sphere for ever.

— Finally, if the initial speed is greater than parabolic velocity, the trajectory is an arc of a hyperbola and likewise the projectile leaves the Earth for ever.

For the case in which the gun is pointed vertically upwards these conclusions are only slightly different ; indeed they are identical when the projectiles are fired at a velocity lower than circular velocity as well as equal or greater than parabolic velocity (Fig. 54). However, when the initial speed is equal to circular velocity the trajectory is an ellipse (in fact it is only a circle in the single case when the firing angle is zero), but this ellipse is in part situated in the interior of the Earth ; the projectile must, therefore, inevitably hit the ground. It is the same if the initial speed lies somewhere between circular and parabolic velocity.

From these considerations it must be concluded that it is impossible to create an artificial satellite if we try to impart to it its final velocity at its moment of departure. In fact, it is only in two instances, when the launching is horizontal, that we can arrive at this theoretical result ; it is clear that in practice this cannot be realised because of the existence of the atmosphere.

Consequently a gun must be formally rejected as a launching instrument not only for artificial satellites but also for those rockets destined to move away from the Earth indefinitely. As well as the obstacle in the shape of the very great air resistance at low altitude — the fantastic increase in heat to which the projectile would be subject would bring about its annihilation in a few fractions of a second — other reasons no less serious justify this rejection. For instance, the enormous speed required would demand an explosive so powerful that it would shatter the gun before the departure of the projectile. Besides, even supposing that the gun and shell were able to resist the tremendous shock of departure, the contents of the projectile would inevitably be reduced to fragments.

Fortunately today scientists have succeeded in perfecting the only suitable method : it consists in raising a rocket to such a height that the air resistance can be considered as negligible and in giving it a steadily increasing speed in such a way that the final velocity can be reached at the highest point on its initial trajectory.

XVIII
ROCKETS

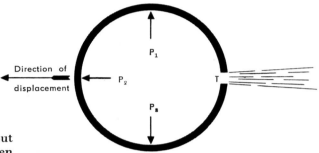

Fig. 55. — Principle of rocket propulsion. *Inside the sphere is compressed gas. The internal pressures cancel each other out ($P_1 = P_3$). But if an opening occurs at T through which the gas may escape, the pressure P_2 is no longer balanced and the globe then begins to move in the direction in which the unbalanced pressure acts.*

The Reaction Principle

The rocket is a machine which has been known for a very long time but which because of an almost incomprehensible reason had only rarely been put to use by ballistic specialists before the second world war. This is even more astonishing since the principle on which it works, that of reaction, is remarkably simple ; an elementary explanation of this may be had by observing how a hollow sphere behaves in a state of equilibrium in space, when there is fuel burning inside in the presence of an oxidant (Fig. 55). The resultant gases exert a pressure on the internal wall but if the sphere is perfectly airtight they in no way modify the state of equilibrium since this pressure has the same value in every direction. On the other hand, if there is a hole at some point on the wall, the gases rush towards the exterior through this opening and the pressure consequently falls on this side ; the pressure acting on the opposite side is no longer balanced and the sphere begins to move. The propulsive force which is thus created internally and which is therefore the pressure exerted on a surface equal to that of the opening is called *thrust* ; it is equal to the flowrate of propellant multiplied by the exhaust gas velocity.

The reaction motor is simply the result of perfecting the rudimentary apparatus we have just been discussing, improvements consisting especially of modifications of those points which could lead to an increase in efficiency. Thus the combustion chamber has been designed in such a way as to allow lateral pressure to increase the downward pressure ; likewise, in order that the expansion of gases may take place under the best possible conditions, the simple orifice has been replaced by a suitably flared nozzle.

In broad outline, a space rocket is composed of a very long cylinder, the top being pointed in shape, and which from top to bottom comprises the following sections (Fig. 56) : a compartment which will contain the payload — there is a tendency today to use the name capsule for this part — a second compartment designed for the rocket's instruments, the tanks containing respectively the fuel and the oxidant, the pipes and pumps, the combustion chamber in which is injected the mixture to be burnt and finally the exhaust nozzle for the burnt gas.

In contrast to the aeroplane which needs air to keep aloft and from which to extract the oxygen indispensable to the combustion of its fuel, the rocket, which carries its own fuel and oxidant, can move in a vacuum. Indeed here is the source of its greatest efficiency for the atmosphere forms the main resistance to its progress. When we consider means of controlling its direction it goes without saying that since in a vacuum a rudder would be totally inoperative an entirely new problem has had to be resolved. The first solution consisted in providing the extremities of the nozzle with small flaps or jet deflectors, the direction of which could be varied. By this means the profile of the combustion chamber was modified to some

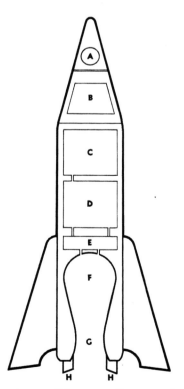

Fig. 56. — Schematic diagram of a rocket.

A. Payload.
B. Instruments.
C. Oxidant.
D. Fuel.
E. Pump.

F. Combustion chamber.
G. Ejection nozzle.
H. Deflector vanes.

U.S. Inf. Service

Capsule of a space rocket. — Photo 63. — A crane is in the process of hoisting the capsule to the top of the gantry where it will be attached to the top of the rocket.

extent, so displacing the point of application of the thrust and bringing about the desired directional effect. Also, by mounting the nozzle on a ball and socket joint, the orientation of the complete jet of burning gas could be made slightly variable ; the effect is the same as in the preceding case but rather more accentuated. Finally, small auxiliary jets, known as vernier rockets, variable at will, may be added to the motor ; by bringing them into play the direction of the resulting thrust may also be varied.

One of the great advantages of the rocket over the shell is the slowness of its departure : no shock is produced and all danger of breakage of the instruments on board is avoided. Its motion is that of a body which, leaving a state of rest, undergoes a permanent force ; it is therefore uniformly accelerated as is, although in the opposite direction, an object falling in free fall. The acceleration ceases, however, as soon as the fuel has been completely consumed ; the rocket then behaves like a passive body launched into space which simply obeys the laws of ballistics. This immediately demonstrates that the final velocity capable of being reached by a rocket at the end of its combustion is directly proportional to the amount of fuel that the rocket is capable of carrying. An improvement in this direction can only be made at the expense of other constituent elements of the rocket, that is to say, the carcass and the payload, and since in the final analysis the rocket is only of interest because of what it can carry, the ideal solution consists in only reducing the dead weight. It is quite obvious that in practice a compromise must be reached.

Final Velocity of a Rocket

The final velocity of a rocket is a function of two fundamental properties : the *exhaust gas velocity* at the exit of the nozzle and the *mass ratio* of the machine, that is to say the ratio which exists between the initial mass of the rocket, that which it possesses on launching, and its final mass, that which remains after the exhaustion of the fuel. The equation which links these elements is simple ; it is written : $V_f = V_e \times \log_e R_m$; V_f, V_e and R_m representing respectively the final velocity, the exhaust gas velocity and the mass ratio. If we take account of the fact that the Napierian logarithm of a number is equal to its decimal logarithm multiplied by 2.3 we can also rewrite the fundamental equation as $V_f = V_e \times 2.3 \log R_m$. It is immediately apparent that to increase the speed of a rocket either the exhaust gas velocity or the mass ratio must be augmented.

The influence of the exhaust gas velocity on the velocity of the rocket is easily understood. Since the thrust of a reaction motor derives from the inequality of pressures which exist at different points in the combustion chamber, this thrust is obviously the more powerful the more rapidly the ejection of the gas — the source of this equilibrium — takes place. For its part, the exhaust gas velocity increases as the heat produced by the combustion of the mixture increases ; therefore, preference must be given to fuels with a very high calorific value. But this exhaust gas velocity is likewise a function of another factor, the lightness of the products of combustion ; if we apply the same energy to heavy molecules and to light molecules it is in fact the latter that will acquire the greatest velocity. Unfortunately, the fuels which give rise to light combustion products are precisely those of slight density ; they demand consequently the use of voluminous tanks which indirectly brings about a reduction in the mass ratio. In fact, we are concerned here again with a problem of quite contradictory data : namely, to find a fuel oxidant mixture of heavy density capable of forming, after combustion, light residual gases.

It is difficult to understand straight away the effect exerted on the final velocity of the rocket by a change in the mass ratio ; it is, in fact, governed by a logarithmic law, the character of which is not familiar to everybody. A few numerical examples, therefore, will make this part of the question more easily understood. If M is the total mass of the rocket (including the payload) without any fuel, and C the mass of the fuel, the mass ratio can be written

$$R_m = \frac{M + C}{M}$$

and immediately it can be seen that a rocket which would carry a weight of fuel equivalent to its own weight (M to be the same value as C) would have a mass ratio equal to 2. If it carried a quantity of fuel weighing twice the weight of the empty machine, its mass ratio would be 3, and so on. The following table demonstrates the variation in mass ratios and their logarithms when the proportion of the fuel carried is modified.

Fraction of the total mass occupied by empty rocket.	1/2 50 %	— 36.8 %	1/3 33.3 %	1/4 25 %	1/5 20 %	1/6 16.7 %	1/7 14.3 %	1/8 12.5 %	1/9 11.2 %	1/10 10 %	1/20 5 %
Fraction of the total mass occupied by fuel.	1/2 50 %	— 63.2 %	2/3 66.7 %	3/4 75 %	4/5 80 %	5/6 83.3 %	6/7 85.7 %	7/8 87.5 %	8/9 88.8 %	9/10 90 %	19/20 95 %
Mass ratio R_m	2	2.718	3	4	5	6	7	8	9	10	20
$\log R_m$	0.301	0.434	0.477	0.602	0.699	0.778	0.845	0.903	0.954	1	3.01
$\log_e R_m$	0.692	1	1.097	1.384	1.608	1.789	1.943	2.077	2.184	2.3	6.9

146

Interesting couclusions may be drawn from this table :

1) The final velocity of the rocket is equal to the exhaust gas velocity when the proportion of fuel is equal to 2/3 of the total mass of the rocket on launch. In fact, in order that V_f should be equivalent to V_e it is necessary for $\log_e R_m$ to he equal to 1, corresponding to a mass ratio of 2.718 i.e. « empty rocket — fuel » in the proportion 36.8% — 63.2% by weight. This would be true, for example of a rocket weighing a ton when empty and carrying 1.718 kg of fuel. The mass ratio is then in fact equal to

$$\frac{1000 + 1718}{1000} \text{ i.e. } 2.718.$$

2) In order to give a rocket a velocity double that of the exhaust gas velocity, it is necessary not just to double the mass ratio but to square it ; similarly to treble this velocity the ratio must be cubed, and so on. This is a direct consequence of the logarithmic nature of the fundamental equation.

3) For this same reason the increase in final velocity is not simply proportional to the increase in the quantity of fuel : it has a more pronounced effect when the change takes place between levels of high mass ratios. In fact, it can be stated that if the proportion of fuel increases by 5% in going from 75% to 80% of the total mass, the final velocity increases from 1.38 times the ejection velocity to 1.6 times this value, whilst if this proportion of fuel increases by 5% between 90% and 95% the corresponding multiplication factor leaps from 2.3 to 6.9. This confirms part of the conclusion reached earlier : to have a high speed a rocket must above all possess the highest possible mass ratio ; that is why it is imperative to make all acceptable sacrifices in the payload and, in a parallel manner, to study the possibilities of employing extremely light metals and alloys in the construction of the body of the rocket.

The V2, which appeared in 1944, moved at a speed almost that of the ejection velocity of its gases, namely 2100 metres per second approximately. Circular and parabolic velocities were therefore far from being attained. During the 5 years which followed this era, constructors built rockets in which the proportion of fuel continued to grow : the mass ratio increased progressively and reached a value of 10, a figure which even today appears to be a maximum. It is difficult to imagine a machine in which less than 10% of the total mass would be reserved for the carcass, the tanks and the payload. Nevertheless, in spite of this fine result no rocket was yet able to reach a speed capable of overcoming gravity. For this it would have been necessary to make a parallel increase in the exhaust gas velocity by quite a considerable amount, that is to say to reach some 3500 m/s, and the means of doing this had not yet been discovered.

The Multi-stage Rocket

However a spectacular idea was about to solve this problem indirectly : the subdivision of the rocket into several sections. Following a principle analogous to that used by an aircraft in flight in jettisoning its empty tanks, the mass ratio can in fact be increased by a progressive reduction of the dead weight, namely by a continuous elimination of everything which has ceased to be of use.

The experiment which was to be the first application of this conception was the launching in America at the beginning of 1949 of two rockets coupled together. A V2 was headed by a considerably smaller rocket, the Wac Corporal, and this assembly was built in such a way as to allow the smaller rocket to be detached at the moment when the carrier rocket had consumed all its fuel. The double system set off, therefore, under the thrust from the single V2 and reached a height of 32,000 m and a velocity of 1600 m/s. The Wac Corporal was then liberated and its fuel set alight. But whereas the V2 had to provide the greatest effort since it had carried up the total weight and had practically gone through the whole of the atmospheric layers, the conditions under which the second rocket was called on to operate were now considerably more favourable. Having already reached a state of motion, namely the velocity reached by the V2, it had only to continue the acceleration without having to struggle against the air resistance and with a mass ratio very much greater than that which the assembly would have had if the carrier rocket had remained attached after the exhaustion of its fuel. In this way the Wac Corporal reached a height of 130,000 m at a velocity of 2250 m/s at the end of combustion. It reached a final height of 400,000 m, after the motor had stopped, by its inertia alone.

Two-stage rocket. — *Photo 64.* — *Schematic outline of the assembly of a space rocket. The first stage is an Atlas rocket, the second an Agena B, and the capsule is one of the Ranger series.*

Ranger capsule

Agena B

Atlas rocket

U.S. Inf. Service.

147

The step or multi-stage rocket, the result of the 1949 experiment, has now become classic : it is composed of a series of several simple rockets, one on top of each other, to form a single body, successive stages being released from behind. The principle of its function is identical with that of the experimental assembly with the difference that the operation of separation can be repeated several times. The velocities acquired by each stage are cumulative and this immediately leads one to believe that the procedure will permit the attainment of any speed with the one condition, namely the provision of a sufficient number of separate units. The application of this line of reasoning, correct in theory, unfortunately comes up against difficulties which increase rapidly. The equipment in a rocket is ultra-delicate, each component part necessitating meticulous setting-up. Each additional stage consequently makes the perfection of the assembly more difficult and increases the risk of break-down or at least inaccuracy of function. One further important point : the payload of each stage (except that of the last), forms in fact the whole of the following stage. Now, as has been said previously concerning the mass ratio, that part in a rocket which is reserved for the payload can only be very small ; put the other way round, this implies that a large final element, the part which must ultimately attain the final velocity necessitates gigantic dimensions in the preceding stages if the number of such stages is multiplied beyond reason. The manufacture of huge rockets has, however, begun and it is probable that the number of stages which at the present moment rarely exceeds four will increase still further in the future.

Whatever happens, the arrival of the multi-stage rocket has introduced a new factor into the calculation of the constituent elements of astronautical space craft, and in order to understand the nature of the problem better, it is necessary to know in the first place the effect of each modification on the final result. Here again, numerical examples will show the consequences of this more clearly.

The example chosen as a basis is that of a three-stage rocket, each section having the same distribution of weight namely :

Fuel	63%
Rocket body and apparatus	27%
Payload	10%

As can be seen, this is a particular case where the mass ratio R_m is equal to 2.7 ; the velocity produced by each stage is therefore that of the exhaust gases. If we suppose this latter equal to 2650 m/s, the successive stages will acquire the following velocities at the end of the combustion of their respective fuels : 2650 m/s, 5300 m/s and 7950 m/s. The latter element will consequently reach circular velocity.

The following table gives the distribution of the weight of the various elements :

	1st stage	2nd stage	3rd stage
Fuel	6300 kg	630 kg	63 kg
Rocket body and apparatus	2700 kg	270 kg	27 kg
Payload	1000 kg	100 kg	10 kg
Totals	10,000 kg	1000 kg	100 kg

and it can be stated that the ratio between the total weight at launch and the final payload is equal to 1000. This figure, the definition of which must not be confused with mass ratio, clearly illustrates what has just been said concerning the considerable proportion in which the dimensions of the various stages increase.

From the preceding table we can also deduce the progress brought about by the use of a multi-stage rocket by comparing the final velocity obtained (7950 m/s) with that reached by a simple rocket of identical weight, namely 10 tons, and carrying the same quantity of fuel, that is 6993 kg or practically 7 tons. Such a rocket would have a mass ratio equal to $\dfrac{10}{10 - 7} = 3.33$

and its velocity would consequently be :
$$V_t = 2650 \times 2.3 \log 3.33$$
$$\text{or} \qquad 2650 \times 2.3 \times 0.522$$
$$\text{that is to say} \quad 3181 \text{ m/s}$$
a result which needs no comment.

What would now happen if, after no modification to the distribution of the weight of the multi-stage rocket, the exhaust gas velocity was varied, increasing to 4000 m/s for example ? After the first stage had functioned the forward velocity would have this same value and, after

Launch of Explorer XIII. — *Photo 65.* — *Departure of a four-stage rocket carrying Explorer XIII on 25 August 1961. This rocket was the 50th satellite placed in orbit by the Americans.*

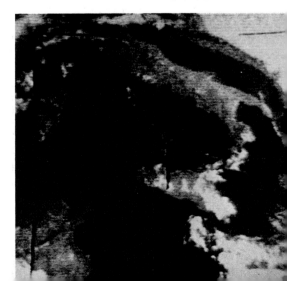

The Mediterranean seen from a height of 800 km. — *Photo 66.* — *Photograph taken above the Mediterranean Sea at a height of 800 km by Tiros III, on 11 September 1961. The satellite was then on its 878th revolution round the Earth.*

148

the application of the second stage, it would reach 8000 m/s. In this case, therefore, two stages would be sufficient to give the same final value and, of great importance, the payload energised with this velocity would be ten times greater.

The following example will show the effect of reducing, by 10 %, the weight of the rocket body as a result of the use of lighter materials, supposing that all this saving in weight can benefit the quantity of fuel. The distribution would then work out as follows :

Fuel	73 %
Rocket body and apparatus	17 %
Payload	10 %

which corresponds to a mass ratio equal to $\dfrac{10}{10 - 7.3} = 3.7$

Supposing now that the exhaust velocity is maintained at its original value (2650 m/s), the successive forward velocities for each stage would then be : 3462 m/s, 6924 m/s and 10,386 m/s.

As a final example, if this saving in weight was applied solely to benefit the payload, the distribution becomes :

Fuel	63 %
Rocket body and apparatus	17 %
Payload	20 %

the mass ratio reverts to its original value, namely 2.7, but the payload is doubled for each stage. If the other hypotheses remain unchanged, the final velocity will remain equal to 7950 m/s but the second stage would weigh 2000 kg, the third 400 kg and the final payload 80 kg.

U.S. Inf. Service.

An Atlas D rocket leaves the pad. — *Photo 68.* — *This launch took place from Cape Canaveral, Florida on 13 September 1961.*

Launch and Stabilization of a Rocket

Having demonstrated the influence of each of the factors on which the functioning of a rocket depends in the examples quoted above, we must now examine how the manufacturers have carried theory into practice and the various improvements that they have brought about.

How, in the first place, does the launching of a space rocket take place ? Since the first object is to send it quickly out of the atmosphere, its path in the layer of air around the Earth is reduced by making it leave vertically. Only at a predetermined altitude does the directional device come into operation and the trajectory incline progressively. In particular, in launching an artificial satellite the calculations are worked out so that the initial trajectory becomes ultimately parallel to the surface of the Earth (Fig. 57).

Immediately following the launch comes the stabilization of the rocket ; special measures must be taken, in fact, to prevent it turning head over heels on its trajectory just like a shell will do if it has not been made to turn rapidly on its axis. The causes of this effect can be summarised in a few words. As long as the rocket is moving through the atmosphere it takes a position such that the air presents a minimum of resistance ; in this way, if a change of direction is demanded it re-assumes its aerodynamic equilibrium as soon as the action causing the turning movement has ceased. But in space where no braking effect exists, that is to say where every action produces effects which last eternally, the rocket behaves very differently : when the directional device is set in motion it acts on the centre of gravity of the rocket and moves its trajectory ; but because of the resulting couple, it at the same time provokes, or at least tends to provoke, the rotation of the whole apparatus around an axis perpendicular to the direction of forward movement. To tell the truth, this undesirable rocking motion may appear sooner for the slightest asymmetry in the elements of the motor would be sufficient to start it off. The remedy is well-known to gunners : it consists in giving the rocket the properties of a gyroscope. It is made to turn on its axis and to bring this about small auxiliary jets placed on the side of the rocket are brought into use. The vernier rockets which we have mentioned earlier can therefore play a double role, that is to say they can act as both directional and stabilizing units at the same time.

U.S. Inf. Service.

Fuel and Oxidants

Of all the problems to which astronautic technicians have devoted many hours of work that of propulsion is the object of their most constant effort for it embodies this most crucial question, the increase in velocity. The forerunner of space rockets, the V2, used methyl alcohol for its fuel and liquid oxygen as the oxidant. This mixture which belongs to

Florida from a height of 740 km. — *Photo 67.* — *Photograph taken by the artificial satellite Tiros III on 14 July 1961 during its 33rd orbit of the Earth. It shows the Gulf of Mexico and Florida. The Tiros series of satellites are designed for meteorological research. They are equipped with normal and television cameras.*

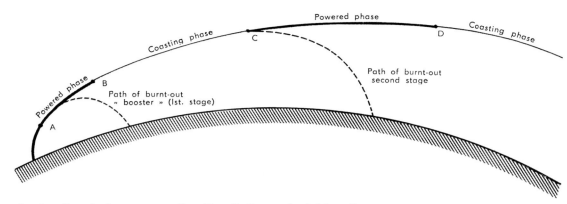

the family of the propergols offered the undeniable advantage of giving rise to a light combustion product, namely water vapour, but its calorific value was not particularly high. However, progress was very quickly made in this respect thanks to the replacement of alcohol by kerosene. As the principal aim was still to obtain light end products, research was specially directed in this field, that is to say towards the possibilities offered by the compounds of simple elefents of very small atomic weight. Chemists, therefore, saw the utilization of fuels derived from simple bodies lighter than carbon, those being (in decreasing order of atomic weight) : boron, beryllium, lithium, helium and hydrogen. Results as new as they were remarkable were the fruit of these researches.

The hydroborons or boranes, substances very similar to hydrocarbons but with higher calorific values, today provide propellants whose manufacture has developed to a considerable degree. This is particularly true of certain compounds of lithium and notably lithium hydride which releases a fantastic heat when burned in the presence of fluorine, the most powerful oxidant known. True, this operation presents serious difficulties, since fluorine attacks practically everything, and substances suitable for the fabrication of fuel tanks and combustion chambers are still very rare. It is not without interest to note that lithium hydride is a solid propellant, a white powder, and that this means quite a different lay-out in the rocket. A curious fact emerges in that by adopting solid propellants one has quite simply gone backwards in time since the original rockets functioned exclusively by means of powder. In fact it was precisely the difficulty encountered in controlling their combustion which led to their being supplanted by liquids. This concern no longer exists for there are now means which permit of a controlled progressive ignition of the powder and furthermore the use of solid propellants makes it possible to pack a higher density of fuel into the tanks. Beryllium has also been the object of much study but its theoretical advantages have not yet materialised into concrete practical results. As for helium, scientists are not greatly concerned with it, since it is an inert gas.

There finally remains hydrogen, the lightest element of all, the use of which had already been envisaged by 'he precursors of astronautics. Although it had originally been declared unsuitable because of its very small density, it has not only re-established itself but is at the present day considered as one of the best of rocket propellants, despite some technical difficulties occasioned by its use ; its preservation and use in a liquid state demand, in fact, a temperature of — 252° C. In order to understand the reason for the reappraisal which has taken place on the subject of hydrogen, we need go no further than look at the fundamental relation

$$V_f = V_e \times \log_e R_m.$$

Since the value of the final velocity is a product of two factors it would be absurd to try to increase one if, as a result of this operation, the other was reduced by the same amount, perhaps even more so. Now this is precisely the result which would have occurred some years ago if hydrogen had been thought of as a fuel. This element is capable of bringing about enormous exhaust velocities but because of its very small density it requires tanks of considerably greater capacity than those used for the classic propergols. The weight of the rocket body, therefore, must be increased to the detriment of that of the other elements, which in turn reduces the mass ratio R_m. However, we must also take account of another very important point : that part of the total weight of the rocket which comprises its real body. The weight of the carcass which until now was very important and represented roughly 25 per cent of the total weight has been reduced little by little and today this proportion is so low as to represent about only 10 per cent. The unfavourable effect on the mass ratio has consequently diminished progressively to such a point even that the increase in exhaust velocity has managed to bring about the reduction of the logarithm of this ratio. The reduction in weight of the carcass has been obtained by using special alloys with a titanium base, a simple element the qualities of which are particularly suited to the needs of astronautics. Its density is considerably lighter than that of iron and it is mechanically stronger.

When a rocket functions with these new types of propellant which release enormous heat, it is quite evident that its combustion chamber and its nozzles must be fashioned accordingly ; this implies the use of material capable of withstanding present day temperatures without melting, temperatures which exceed that of the melting point of graphite, namely 3700° C. In this realm likewise technicians have made important strides since they have succeeded in increasing the thermal resistance of graphite by incorporating with it other rare elements such as for example vanadium and zirconium.

Finally, one cannot speak of future space projects without mentioning modes of propulsion which are already seriously envisaged by scientists and which have recourse to a new aspect of power, atomic energy. Nothing, of course, has so far been accomplished in this respect for the difficulties of taming this energy, so tremendously greater than any other, are enormous. A completely new technique is in the process of being created in this direction and there is not the slightest doubt that in astronautics as in all other domains of science a real revolution will take place ; as far as the problem of propulsion of rockets is concerned it promises sensational surprises.

XIX

LIFE
ON BOARD A ROCKET

To reach the Moon by means of a rocket is one thing. To send a human being there is quite another ; and if the first has already been achieved, in the sense at least that the object launched has not made a soft landing but crashed on to the lunar surface — there is no certainty about the second. The human machine is unfortunately not governed by the rigorous laws of mechanics and its resistance cannot be reinforced by methods analogous to those which are suitable for metallic and synthetic substances.

The description made elsewhere of the lunar surface has clearly shown the dangers to which astronauts will be exposed when they arrive on the Moon. Now if we examine all the aspects which the journey itself presents, it is also fraught with risks and perils.

Acceleration and Deceleration

For a long time the question was asked, how would man manage to support the tremendous acceleration occurring in a rocket. Today this question would seem to be rather superfluous since several human beings have already proved by their exploits in space that the organism can withstand the experience ; but we must not forget that these first astronauts were extremely carefully chosen and trained for a long time. Their performances are not therefore attainable by just anyone.

A powerful acceleration creates in the human body a sudden rush of blood and if the axis of the body lies in the same direction in which the force is acting, the blood is driven towards the lower part of the abdomen and the limbs thus causing a diminution of pressure in the arteries of the brain. The result is the black-out well-known to pilots of aircraft, taking the form of a transient blindness and sometimes fainting. If the acceleration is exceptionally violent, the danger becomes very great for it is capable of causing internal lesions, coma and even death. The time during which the acceleration acts is a determining factor ; animals on which experiments have been made in this respect have withstood for 2 minutes an acceleration corresponding to 10 or even 20 times the force of gravity ; in contrast, others have died after 10 minutes because a continous force equal to 10 g had been inflicted on them (as gravity is represented by the letter g, it is usual to designate by 2 g and 3 g forces twice or three times as great).

The danger of excessive acceleration of too long a duration need not fortunately be over-emphasised on a space rocket for its fuel is always consumed very quickly. Nevertheless careful precautions must be taken. In the first place, the astronaut must be positioned perpendicular to the direction of flight ; it is quite natural,

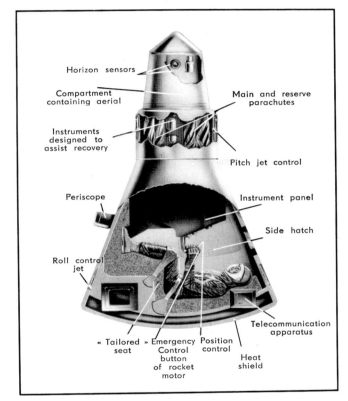

Horizon sensors

Compartment containing aerial

Main and reserve parachutes

Instruments designed to assist recovery

Pitch jet control

Periscope

Instrument panel

Side hatch

Roll control jet

« Tailored » seat

Emergency Control button of rocket motor

Position control

Telecommunication apparatus

Heat shield

U.S. Inf. Service.
Interior of a capsule. — Photo 69. — Artist's impression showing the arrangement of a capsule to be fitted to the rockets of the Project Mercury series.

Anti-g suits. — Photo 70. — Astronauts ready for a journey into space.
U.S. Inf. Service.

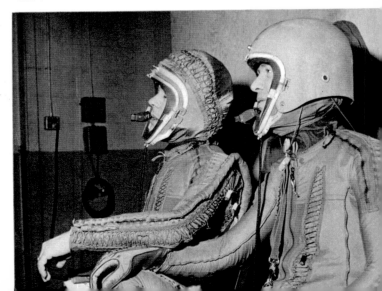

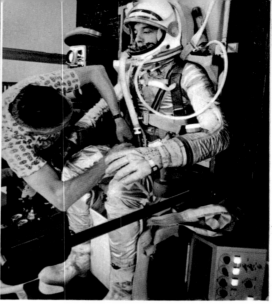

therefore, for the lying position to be taken at departure. Furthermore, he must wear a so-called anti-g suit, that is to say a special garment provided with pockets or pads which are capable of increasing inflation as the acceleration of the rocket becomes greater ; it compresses the abdomen as well as the limbs and drives the blood back towards the brain. One good solution consists in using a moulded couch following perfectly the shape of the occupant and turning it on its side so that the back of the latter is horizontal.

Astronauts can be trained in centrifuges, i.e., cabins fixed at the end of a rotating arm and capable of being turned at enormous speeds. The trainees are thus subjected to centrifugal forces corresponding to accelerations reaching 12 g, that is to an excess weight somewhat greater than that of a rocket at departure ; the latter is usually about 10 g.

Effects which occur as a result of braking or, as it is also called, during deceleration, are identical in every way to those caused by acceleration. No extra measure of protection need therefore be taken except possibly the positioning of the body which should be turned around. However this change usually operates automatically since the rocket is turned around before landing.

Weightlessness

Following the effects of excessive acceleration which characterize the beginning of a space voyage comes a totally opposed phenomenon known as weightlessness. It appears immediately the motive power ceases, that is to say at that moment when the rocket behaves like an inert projectile. In fact, contrary to what many people believe the astronaut then finds himself in a state of *relative* zero gravity. One cannot do better than to compare this situation to that which exists inside a lift when the cable is broken. Everything in it yields completely to the pull of gravity — for this exists all the time — and if a traveller in the lift were to try to let go of an object the latter would remain in its place and would seem, therefore, to refuse to drop. In fact, it continues to drop but as its fall takes place with everything else around it, it cannot be perceived inside the lift.

The physiological effects caused by weightlessness also appear capable of being withstood by the human being, as the prowess of the first astronauts has shown. Unfortunately, there can be no question on this count of intensive training for nothing is more difficult than the creation of a state of weightlessness ; to some extent this can be felt by the parachutist in free flight and on a very much smaller scale by the diver. It can just be noticed by passengers descending the Big Dipper. Actually it has been brought about, but only for 10 seconds or so, on board an aeroplane in which the pilot describes a portion of a parabolic trajectory similar to that traced by a shell in space. The sensations experienced by those living these short moments of weightlessness are very varied ; some feel a real distress accompanied by nausea whilst others feel themselves in a state of well-being. From all accounts, habit seems to play a decisive role.

In fact, it is perfectly possible to get some idea of what life on board a space rocket will be like during the periods of ballistic flight. The occupiers will not be able to move around except by the help of hooks unless, of course, they wear magnetic or suction operated foot-gear. Possibly they will be able to use wing-like paddles and to fly in a fashion in the interior of the cabins. They will not even be able to drink out of a glass or to pour water out of a bottle unless a blow is given to the latter ; but even then the liquid as it comes out will remain in suspension in the cabin in the form of globules. On the other hand they will be able to drink by sucking the liquid through a straw and they will have no difficulty in swallowing since gravity hardly enters into this physiological phenomenon. Finally, deprived of all idea of up or down, they will not know the difference between standing up or lying down and to raise something will be for them devoid of meaning. As the slightest bump between them will send them from one end to the other of the cabin, they will be obliged when sleeping to attach themselves to a rigid point.

Temperature, Air Pressure and Food

It seems pretty clear that if the instruments contained in the Russian Venus rocket ceased prematurely to function it is becouse the temperature inside the capsule hat not been perfectly stabilised. This problem is, in fact, one of major importance and the difficulties in solving it are abundantly clear when one realises that in the choice of reflecting material used for covering the outer surfaces, account must be taken of the fantastic temperature difference which exists between the face turned towards the Sun and that turned towards the opposite side. One further question can also be asked : at what point do the enormous variations in temperature which characterize the regions close to the Earth become dangerous for a space rocket ? It is known, in fact, that the temperature of the atmosphere does not decrease regularly, as was once imagined, with altitude. This only takes place up to about 10,000 m, but it then remains stationary at about —55° C. as far as 25,000 m. It then increases and approaches 0° C. at 50,000 m, decreasing once more to —90° C. at 85,000. Finally, it once again begins to increase considerably, passing 1000° C. at a height of between 500 and 1000 km. However, these calorific variations cannot affect in any way the shell of a rocket for the temperature of gas molecules depends directly upon their kinetic energy ; that possessed by air molecules at very great height is therefore only large because the velocity of their thermal agitation is large. However, as the pressure is minimal at great height the collisions of molecules against the walls of the rocket are infinitely rarer than near ground level and the heat which they can release during these collisions is consequently extremely small, if not negligible.

Air conditioning inside a space cabin likewise poses an important problem. The necessity for a light shell withstanding the least amount of stress implies an internal pressure reduced to the smallest value compatible with the conditions of life. Experts estimate that we can be satisfied with half the normal atmospheric pressure as long as this reduction is compensated for by an increase in the oxygen percentage. In fact, the solution to be adopted ought to be very similar to that which takes place on submarines where the same air is continually being regenerated. In this way one can foresee particularly the absorption by chemical means of the air rejected by the lungs ; as for the water vapour coming from breath and perspiration, it will be changed into drinking water.

The same principle of regeneration will be applied to the problem of food. Space doctors are trying in this respect to select a concentrated food capable of making the astronauts live according to a closed cycle. Certain algae fulfil this condition for they constitute a complete food ; besides they develop easily and rapidly, their needs being limited to carbon dioxide and a little fat, two elements which the passengers in the rocket will be able to give them. In return they release oxygen which can then be breathed by the travellers.

Vibration

A double problem of a physiological nature but of quite different character must equally be considered : that of noise and the total absence of noise, two phenomena to which man is equally sensitive. The absolute silence into which the passengers of a space rocket will

U.S. Inf. Service.

Redstone rocket. — *Photo 73. — The launch of the Redstone rocket from Cape Canaveral on 5 May 1961, carrying inside the capsule (named Freedom 7) America's first astronaut Alan B. Shepard Jr. The capsule, weighing a ton, reached a height of 185 km and came down in the Atlantic Ocean 486 km from the launching point after a 15-minute flight.*

Centrifuge. — *Photo 74. — An arm of the centrifuge installed at the Naval and Air Research Institute in Pennsylvania.*

Weightlessness. — *Photo 75. — Effects of « relative zero gravity » obtained on board an aeroplane whose pilot is following a parabolic trajectory similar to that of a shell fired into space.*

U.S. Inf. Service.

U.S. Inf. Service.

be plunged as soon as the motor stops, constitutes a serious preoccupation of the doctors and it is probable that training for this depressing situation will be indispensable. It is useful to remember in this respect certain observations made in places which are strictly soundproof such as the chambers of silence where measuring apparatus of high accuracy is preserved from every type of vibration. The operators were at times the victims of mental troubles because they had remained there too long.

On the other hand excessive sound vibrations including ultrasonic and subsonic sounds, can only be supported by human beings with great difficulty. It was for this reason that the first American astronaut, Alan B. Shepard, was on the point of pressing his rocket escape button, so insupportable were the vibrations during the powered phase of his flight. However, this incident led the constructors to improve the next rocket considerably. The re-entry of a rocket into the atmosphere can likewise cause very painful effects on the organism, although these are less serious. This occurs when the centre of thrust of the forces of aerodynamic braking do not coincide with the centre of gravity of the capsule and the latter then becomes the focus of very rapid oscillations.

From all this we must conclude that the sound proofing of the capsule represents one of the essential conditions of success in a rocket voyage. The wearing of a special helmet also seems indispensable.

Meteorites

The danger which an encounter with meteorites would cause to space navigators has been the object of numerous experiments. To determine the chances of collision, scientists launched artificial satellites provided with meteorite detectors, that is to say with special apparatus directly connected to a radio transmitter on board whose function was to transmit the information in one way or another. Such a detector might even be a simple microphone placed on the outside of the rocket which would record the noise of the impacts. Equally it could be composed of a set of metallic grilles made of very fine wire which are broken by contact with a meteorite ; the destruction of a grille causes a signal to be transmitted. Another system consists in analysing at regular intervals the erosion caused by the small meteorites on a conducting layer which covers certain parts of the rocket ; the signal transmitted by the transmitter takes account in this case of the variation of electrical resistance of this layer. Finally, some detectors are real recording counters, the recording being made on magnetic tape ; this process of modulation of the transmission makes not only the number of meteorites encountered known but also the energy with which the collision is produced. The results obtained, whatever the methods used, are in agreement and moreover rather unexpected : the number of meteorites is considerably less than had been feared. It can be considered therefore that the risk of the destruction of a rocket through collision with these celestial bodies is very slight indeed.

Radiation

Dangers of yet another category threaten our astronauts : those caused by the radiations of all types which traverse space. Obviously travellers ought to be able to protect themselves from ultra-violet rays by wearing protective glasses ; it will also be necessary to provide the rocket portholes with the same type of filters. As for cosmic rays already mentioned, we do not yet know precisely their harmful effects for they only arrive on the Earth considerably attenuated. They can be considered as a radiation of particles, hydrogen nuclei and protons, emanating from an ill-defined region of space — probably to a great extent from the Sun — and endowed with a velocity near that of light. Arriving in the atmosphere, they collide with the molecules of air and give rise to further particles which are the ones to reach us. Artificial satellites have, therefore, been launched with the intention of studying the nature of cosmic rays ; not only have they provided certain precise details in this respect but they made a sensational discovery, the existence of a double belt of radiation around our sphere. The average distance to the region occupied by the first belt is some 3000 km, whilst the second is about 25,000 km away. The American physicist J. Van Allen, who studied these very special radiations and who has given his name to the radiation belts, believes them to be formed by a mixture of electrons and protons which have accumulated around the Earth as a result of the presence of its magnetic field (Fig. 58). They are probably such as to cause injury to human beings, but it seems that as the spacecraft possess enormous velocities there will be scarcely any danger in crossing the Van Allen belts. If it is thought, however, that it would be dangerous to cross them, the belts can be avoided by escaping from the Earth at one of the Poles since the radiations do not exist at these points.

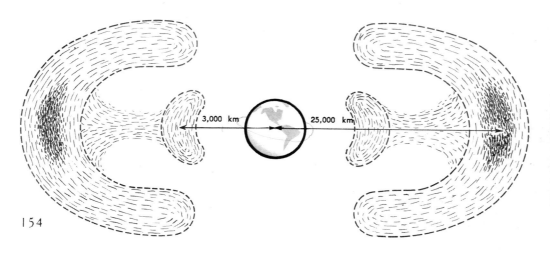

Fig. 58. — Van Allen belts. Section in space in a plane passing through the geomagnetic axis of the Earth. The crescent-shaped outlines, representing the inner and outer belts respectively, resemble the magnetic tracings obtained when iron filings are sprinkled on a sheet of glass held over a magnet.

XX

STAGES
ON THE JOURNEY

The Four Phases of the Lunar Journey – Characteristic Velocity

A journey to the Moon such as is envisaged in its final form comprises four distinct phases : departure from the Earth, arrival on our satellite and subsequent landing, departure from the Moon and finally return to the Earth. The fuel needs demanded by the first phase have already been studied ; those of the following two phases, although equal to each other, are fortunately much reduced. In fact, the impact velocity on the lunar surface of a body attracted by the Moon assuming it left a state of rest in a determined point in space is the same as that at which this body must be launched from the Moon in order to reach the aforementioned point. But since the landing must be made at zero velocity as it is necessay to avoid destruction, the rocket must be braked until it stops, a manœuvre which in space requires the same energy which originally brought about the velocity in question. The only difference lies in the direction of the thrust of the gases, which is obviously reversed ; the reactors which are used for this braking are generally called retro-rockets. Furthermore, as the lunar gravity is six times weaker than that of the Earth, the critical velocities (circular, parabolic and hyperbolic velocities) are likewise smaller and this situation favourably influences the consumption of fuel.

The final landing on the Earth deserves a special study for the atmosphere is at one and the same time a source of very serious danger and a stroke of luck for the astronaut : a danger because if the space rocket encounters the layer of air at too great a speed it cannot escape destruction through heat and fusion ; a stroke of luck because if the braking action of the molecules of gas is opportunely turned to profit, an important economy in fuel may be realised.

In order to highlight the total amount of energy expended in each one of these four phases, the specialists had recourse to an idea of a rather peculiar nature, the *characteristic velocity*, whose meaning we must endeavour to understand. Since in the final analysis the energy spent is used to create a determined velocity one can logically evaluate the total cost of a space mission by translating it in terms of velocity ; for this it is enough to add simply to the initial velocity the extra velocities which the mission requires as it goes along. If the necessary energy for these contributions is transmitted to the rocket in an uninterrupted fashion, the characteristic velocity is simply equal to the final velocity ; this is the case of a multi-stage rocket in which the stages function one after the other without any interruption. But if at any period the motors temporarily cease to function, the characteristic velocity is nothing more than a mathematical sum, representing no real velocity ; nevertheless, it very conveniently reflects the total expenditure of energy and constitutes an excellent element of comparison. It is in this form that it appears for a return journey to a planet together with a stop on the latter. In any case, however, the characteristic velocity of a given mission can only be rather approximately estimated since it depends on a number of factors which vary according to the solutions adopted ; a journey to the Moon is significant in this respect.

In order to evaluate the characteristic velocity of this journey, the major portion, that is to say the velocity of departure from the ground, must first of all be calculated. As a fundamental condition this velocity must always be high enough for the rocket to reach one of the points in space where the lunar attraction is equal to that exerted by the Earth. In fact, having passed this point it is subject to the predominant action of our satellite and it is capable of falling normally towards it. Although necessary, this condition is not however sufficient, as will be seen further on, except in the purely theoretical case when the Earth-Moon trajectory is a straight line. The « neutral point » or « point of equal attraction » is situated at a distance of 9/10 of the way from our sphere. In fact, according

U.S. Inf. Service.

Recovery of the capsule. — *Photo 76. — The capsule containing the American astronaut John H. Glenn is brought back on board, 20 February 1962, having made three orbits of the Earth. The total distance covered was 130,000 km in 4 hr 56 min. Apogee 261.3 km ; perigee 159.2 km.*

to Newton's law, anything situated at this place is subjected to a double action : on the one hand, since the mass of the Earth is 81 times that of our satellite it is attracted 81 times more strongly by the Earth than by the Moon ; but on the other hand, being nine times nearer the latter it is likewise attracted by it 9^2 times more. The two actions consequently cancel out, so that if our satellite is situated at its mean distance from the Earth the neutral point is 345,000 km away from the centre of the Earth and is therefore no more than 38,000 km from that of the Moon (Fig. 59).

It is quite obvious that there will be more to it than getting the lunar rocket to the neutral point at the precise moment when its velocity is zero. The risk would be too great, for the slightest fault in the functioning of the apparatus which might result in too small a velocity would make it inevitably fall back again towards the Earth. Besides the chances of a failure occurring are a direct function of the number of neutral points and there are as many of these as there are possible trajectories with constantly changing positions as for all heavenly bodies. Furthermore this state of affairs shows quite clearly the impossibility in which one finds oneself of determining in a straightforward way the initial velocity to give to a rocket destined to reach the Moon. However, it is calculated to be about 11 km/s, that is to say that it is almost equal to the parabolic velocity at ground level. In fact, in the estimation of the characteristic velocity, this last value (11.2 km/s) is normally used, which provides an indispensable margin of safety.

Fig. 59. — Relative strenghth of terrestrial and lunar gravity. *The neutral point or point of equal attraction lies about 9/10 of the distance along a straight line joining the Earth and Moon, that is 345,600 km from the centre of the Earth and 38,400 km from that of our satellite, assuming that the latter is at its mean distance from us.*

Beyond the neutral point the velocity of the space rocket begins once more to increase, under the action of the gravitational attraction of the Moon, and at impact with the latter it reaches a value practically equal to the lunar parabolic velocity (2.3 km/s). Since the energy which will be used to reduce this to zero is the same as to create it, the relative characteristic velocity of the Earth-Moon journey, not including a return but a properly executed lunar landing, is 11.2 + 2.3 km/s, that is 13.5 km/s. This sum comprises the exclusively mathematical notion defined earlier on since the rocket never reaches such a velocity at any moment.

The calculation of the characteristic velocity for the return journey is not as simple and the reason for this has already been mentioned. Two factors are equally involved but if the value of the first is known (2.3 km/s for the departure from the Moon), that of the second is relatively difficult to determine for it depends essentially on the method used for re-entry into our atmosphere. If the procedure decided on in advance takes no account of the presence of the layer of air, this second factor would have the same value as the parabolic velocity at the surface and in this case the characteristic velocity for the return journey would be identical with that of the journey to the Moon. The total characteristic velocity of the Earth-Moon-Earth mission would then reach the colossal value of 27 km/s. On the contrary, if a procedure were to be put into operation of using the atmosphere as an ideal brake, that is to say not needing the consumption of any energy, the total sum would only be 15.8 km/s. This question will be examined further on in some greater detail, but it can already be easily understood that a reasonable solution of the problem lies somewhere between the extreme values mentioned.

A Lunar Shot

Although the expression « lunar shot » has now entered popular parlance, care must be taken not to compare in too narrow a fashion the flight of projectiles towards the Moon with ballistic shots from conventional guns. Possibly they might be likened to naval gun-fire where both gun and objective are in motion. Nevertheless the methods are very different by virtue of the infinitely greater distances which in astronautics separate the points of departure and arrival, and include, therefore, time as a factor of prime importance. Another problem therefore arises as crucial as that of the consumption of fuel, namely the high degree of accuracy of the shot.

As we know, the Moon advances in its orbit at a velocity of 1 km/s. In one hour it traverses therefore, 3600 km, that is to say a distance rather greater than its diameter (3470 km), and this immediately shows that if the rocket, pointed at the moment of departure towards the centre of the Moon, arrives half an hour early or late, it will miss its target. This conclusion may come as a surprise, for in too simple a fashion it may be thought that from the moment a body enters the zone where the lunar attraction is predominant, its trajectory is deviated so as to land inevitably on the Moon. Stated in this way, this conception is in no way correct, for it makes no mention of the velocity with which the rocket arrives, whereas the effect of this factor is of great importance. Just like terrestrial gravity lunar gravity becomes weaker as the distance at which it is acting is increased and this is likewise the same obviously for parabolic velocity. The latter is no more than 2 km/s at 500 km from the centre of the Moon ; at 1000 km it is equal to 1.9 km/s and at 6000 km it is no greater than roughly 1 km/s. This means, amongst other things, that a body endowed with a velocity higher than a mere 1000 m/s and passing 6000 km above the Moon without travelling straight towards it, does not undergo enough attraction to lead it towards the Moon (Fig. 60).

As it turns around the Earth our satellite is also the object of another displacement : since its orbit is elliptical it comes closer to us and moves further away alternately, and as the distance between the maximum and minimum

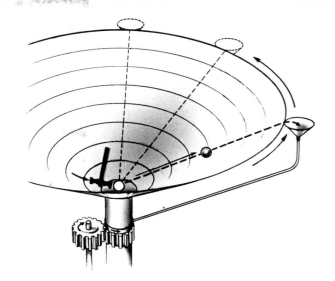

Fig. 60. — Analogy of a lunar shot. *In order to take account of the difficulties facing the launching of a lunar rocket, imagine the following experiment. A small bowl turns at a non-uniform speed around a cone-shaped large dish to which it remains constantly attached. A ball lies at the base of the dish and must be driven from this point at the appropriate speed and direction so that it just falls into the bowl and remains there. Consequently the ball must arrive at the edge of the large upturned cone at the precise moment when the small cone is passing this spot. Its speed must not be too great otherwise it will jump out of the small receptacle under the influence of its own impetus.*

distance is never less than 40,000 km, this variation also assumes a serious importance. Besides, one can immediately see the advantage in undertaking the journey to the Moon when the latter is at its perigee.

Although of lesser importance, all the other motions of our satellite must equally be taken into account and not even its phases can be ignored. The attraction taking place on the Earth in the direction of the Moon varies very slightly according to the relative position of the Sun ; it is, for example, at a maximum at the new Moon since at this period the solar attraction is directly added to that of our satellite. In fact, these variations give rise to the same effect as if the terrestrial gravity changed slightly and periodically in value.

In brief, the motions of the Moon affect the parameters of a lunar shot in a very complex manner. The enormous importance of the time factor clearly appears in the following example. It is only necessary for the launch velocity of a rocket destined to reach the Moon to increase from 11.2 km/s to 11.4 km/s, an increase in velocity of only 2%, for the duration of the journey to go from 43 to 30 hours, which represents a reduction in time of 33%. This is indeed considerably greater than the simple half hour which was enough to miss the target...

To tell the truth, if one were to try and resolve the problem in the manner used in classical ballistics, the chances of reaching the Moon would be practically non-existent. It is therefore necessary to proceed in a totally different way : the ideal trajectory must be worked out minutely, in space and time, taking into account all the astronomical elements concerning the relative motions of the Earth and the Moon at the chosen epoch ; at the same time the exact duration of the journey must be fixed and more accurately the velocity given to the space rocket at each instant must be defined ; and finally, the rocket must be forced to follow strictly the predetermined programme. Remote control, this remarkable application of the principles of radio and precise mechanics, is today in the process of satisfying these demands.

The sensational success obtained on 12 and 13 September 1959 by the Russian scientists who sent the first man-made object to the Moon is well known. This exploit was only made possible thanks to radio guidance : during the greater part of its journey Lunik II remained in radio contact with terrestrial stations which followed its movement ; in this way it was able to be remotely controlled to a very great distance away from our sphere. It will be recalled not without interest that this same Lunik II just before it hit the Moon transmitted the signals which allowed the conclusion to be drawn that there was no lunar magnetic field.

Space Velocities

Three sorts of velocity can be theoretically envisaged for the launch of a lunar rocket, elliptical, parabolic and hyperbolic velocities, but in fact two only need be considered for parabolic velocity being placed exactly at the limit separating the two others is almost unattainable.

Those velocities which give rise to an elliptical trajectory offer the not unimportant advantage of demanding less fuel. Besides, if it is only a question of bringing the rocket to the vicinity of our satellite without a landing, they allow it to be eventually recovered since the latter returns of necessity to the Earth (Figs. 61, 62 and 63). However, they present a serious inconvenience which detracts from the accuracy of the shot. In fact, the only possible elliptical trajectories correspond to initial velocities at least equal to 99% of the parabolic velocity. This means therefore extremely elongated ellipses for which the length of the major axis rapidly tends towards infinity as the elliptical velocity approaches parabolic velocity. The different trajectories therefore become progressively further and further away from the object to be reached (Fig. 64).

From this same point of view hyperbolic velocities present an undeniable advantage which counterbalances the inconvenience of demanding considerably more fuel. In fact, if a rocket is launched at a velocity slightly greater than parabolic, the slightest error made moves the trajectory proportionately further away from the objective, but when the hyperbolic velocities differ more and more from parabolic velocity, the separation decreases much more rapidly than in the preceding case.

In reality, the best solution consists in adopting a hyperbolic velocity slightly greater than parabolic velocity. This was the decision arrived at by the American and Russian scientists for the launch of the lunar rockets Pioneer IV and Luniks I and II : the velocity of the latter rocket has been estimated at about 101% of parabolic velocity.

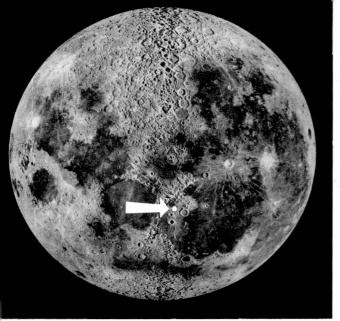

Point of impact of Lunik II. — Photo 77. — The place of the impact is indicated by the arrow.

Having determined the date of the launch of a lunar rocket, taking account of the most favourable astronomical epoch, having also finally fixed the initial velocity, the experts have then to calculate all the elements of the ideal trajectory for the rocket along with the corresponding velocities. Once the rocket is launched the problem consists in simply measuring its position and velocity constantly, comparing the latter with the predetermined velocity and eventually causing the operation of one or other motor to carry out the necessary corrections.

Such a method would have been unthinkable 30 years ago if only for the reason that it would have been impossible then to have measured a minute interval of time such as that demanded by the needs of astronautics. Today, electronic computers solve problems in a matter of moments which require hours on the part of a human being ; electronic watches provide the time to a millionth of a second, radar measures distance not only instantaneously but with an extraordinary accuracy, and remote command systems switch on and off with no difficulty electronic circuits which may be tens or even hundreds of thousands of kilometres away.

Tracking Networks

Since the rotation of our sphere only complicates matters, it would not simply be a matter of entrusting the control of the rocket to a single station on Earth. A network is necessary comprising many tracking stations spread out on the greatest possible scale and using modern electronic apparatus of extreme accuracy : receivers, comparators, computers and transmitters capable of encoding and sending orders to the rocket. As for the latter, it must likewise be equipped with numerous pieces of apparatus capable of receiving these orders, intrepreting them and instantly transmitting them to the appropriate motors ; thus remote commands may control not only the start of rocketmotors, but also the orientation of nozzles, the duration of a motor operation and any other guidance operation.

One aspect of modern science which has been seen to grow in these last few years, cybernetics, lends today considerable aid to astronautics. It allows the development of every possible method of endowing certain machines with the capability of taking decisions for themselves ; the electronic tortoise which moves of its own accord in a specific direction because it is provided with the mechanism which makes it point itself automatically towards light, is the narrow classic example of cybernetic behaviour. There is nothing to prevent one imagining in the future the replacement of many of the remote guidance operations by auto-guidance based on the principles of cybernetics. The manœuvres of Lunik III which orientated itself in a suitable manner to take photographs of the other side of the Moon were nothing more than an application of cybernetics.

Re-entry

Of the problems which still remain to be solved before a lunar journey can become a reality there is one of so much importance that the experts have spent a good deal of thought over it from the beginning of the era of space rockets ; it concerns re-entry into our atmosphere. Data which have already been outlined above have shown that from many points of view it is necessary to abandon the idea of bringing a rocket down to Earth on the assumption that our sphere was devoid of atmosphere ; the expense of fuel would be absolutely prohibitive and the idea unacceptable even if the means were available. On the other hand, the atmosphere can only be used as a brake with extreme care at the risk of disaster ; thus we could not allow the capsule to return vertically towards the ground ; the speed with which it would cross the progressively denser layers of air would cause such heat that it would be burnt up in a very small amount of time. In fact, it is the angle at which the rocket strikes our atmosphere that is the predominant factor.

One of the precursors of astronautics, the German physicist Hohmann, proposed many years ago the following method, which in fact avoids this abrupt re-entry into the atmosphere : the capsule strikes the latter tangentially and at such a height that the air resistance, although creating a relatively weak heating effect, appreciably brakes the speed of arrival. The trajectory is thus modified and takes up the shape of a very elongated ellipse ; the rocket sets off again towards space as it circles the Earth and returns once more at a lower height so that the atmosphere which it re-encounters is denser and so accentuates the braking effect. From this point, the process continues in the same fashion : the successive elliptical trajectories are progressively less elongated whilst the velocity decreases and this continues right up to the moment when re-entry into the atmosphere and a landing on the Earth by parachute is possible. This method involving the so-called Hohmann orbits is undeniably attractive from the economic point of view for theoretically it does not require any consumption of fuel. Unfortunately, it is as long as it is delicate and consequently very difficult to bring about ; the slightest error which might cause the rocket to penetrate prematurely a too-dense layer of air would be sufficient to result in catastrophe (Fig. 65).

More recently space scientists have discovered that there is a re-entry « corridor » through which an astronaut may be safely brought, starting the descent approximately one orbit away. The corridor is reached through the use of retro-rockets fired at a predetermined moment causing the capsule to enter the atmosphere at a precisely determined angle ; the final landing is then by parachute.

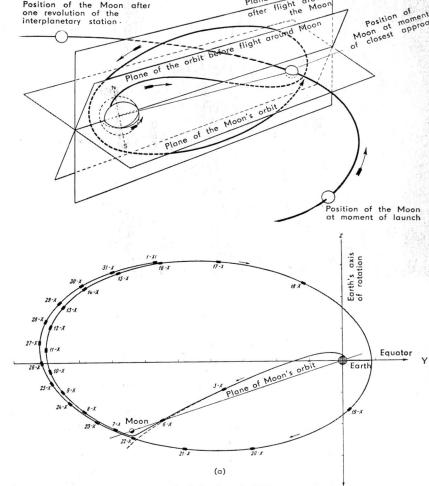

Fig. 61. — The trajectory of Lunik III (4 October 1959). *The launch velocity of Lunik III was elliptical since the aim of the operation was to go round the Moon, but it approached to within 99% of parabolic velocity. The duration of the journey was therefore appreciably longer (60 hours) than that of Lunik II (36 hours). In fact the rocket passed further beyond the Moon than had been predicted, reaching a maximum distance from the Earth of 470,000 km.*

The trajectory was so calculated that the gravitational pull of the Moon caused a certain amount of rotation of the rocket's orbital plane, in order to bring the rocket back to the same terrestrial hemisphere. When a rocket is launched from the northern hemisphere, it will return in fact to the southern hemisphere, and this had to be avoided to allow the Russian tracking stations to maintain continuous contact with the Moon rocket.

It is however in the shape of rocket bodies and the choice of the materials used in their construction that the most marked progress has been made recently ; capsules orbiting the Earth have been recovered successfully without damage. The result is undeniably sensational but it does not completely solve the problem in its general form. Artificial satellites possess, in fact, velocities of about 8 km/s whereas space probes returning from the Moon will arrive in the neighbourhood of the Earth at some 11 km/s and this difference is considerable when one thinks in terms of crossing the heat barrier. The thermal obstacle which is called by this name by analogy with the sound barrier is, in fact, formed by a cushion of air pushed along in front of the body in motion and which, arising from the enormous compression which it receives, aquires a fantastic temperature, some 10,000°. The problem which must be solved is consequently that of insuring the removal of this tremendous heat into the surrounding atmosphere ; it is essentially different from that which occurs in aviation where the aim is to avoid losses of energy caused by displacement of air ; the aeroplane must be aerodynamic and this is why its leading edges are given a streamlined structure and its fuselage a pointed shape. In astronautics on the contrary, re-entry into the atmosphere is characterised by an excess of energy which must be got rid of ; therefore interest lies in adopting forms which are quite clearly anti-aerodynamic and this is why the shape of the modern rocket is rounded. This particular outline allows 99% of the heat produced to be eliminated.

The constituent material of rockets has also been the subject of much study and has been very considerably improved upon during the last few years. In fact, it was necessary to find a substance which was both capable of resisting the considerable mechanical stress to which it would be exposed and of being a bad conductor of heat to prevent the latter penetrating into the interior of the capsule. From this point of view the ideal solution would lie in being able to manufacture a material which when the temperature is raised to a very high degree, would become the seat of an endothermic (heat absorbing) reaction capable of improving its mechanical qualities. Today, this double result has been partly achieved since technologists have succeeded in perfecting certain compounds, notably ceramics, the properties of which come very close to the ideal qualities.

A new technique has also brought appreciable progress to the problem of re-entry ; it consists in using the excess heat to burn away or ablate a portion of the capsule intentionally. To this end, the latter is covered with an outer surface designed to melt completely and

Fig. 62. — Trajectory described by Lunik III as seen as a projection from the vernal equinox (first point of Aries).

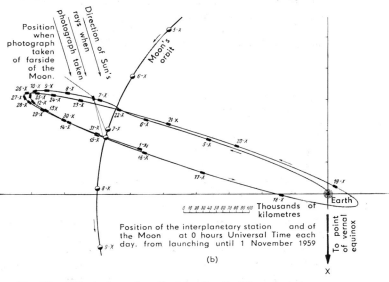

(b)

Fig. 63. — Trajectory described by Lunik III projected on the plane of the Earth's equator.

Fig. 64. — Elliptical lunar trajectories. *An ellipse which passes close to the Earth and to the Moon is so elongated that it approaches a parabola. For small increases in velocity the elliptical trajectories elongate in constantly increasing proportion and consequently they rapidly diverge from the Moon.*

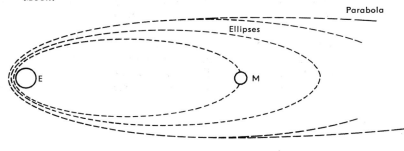

U.S. Inf. Service.

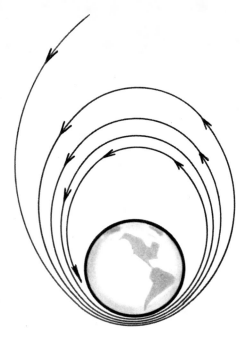

Fig. 65. — Hohmann orbits. *The space rocket encounters the atmosphere tangentially and at great height. It therefore only touches lightly the thin air layers which sufficiently brake its speed so that it describes an elongated ellipse around the Earth. It then re-enters the atmosphere but nearer the surface so that the braking effect is increased, being close to the perigee of the following elliptical trajectory. The process continues until the speed is sufficiently reduced to allow a landing.*

Recovery of a capsule. — *Photo 78. — Capture in flight, 14 November 1961, of the capsule from Discoverer XVII by a C 119 aircraft, when the space rocket had finished its 31st orbit of the Earth. Is was the third successful operation of this kind. The capsule weighed 136 kg.*

is of course thermally isolated from the internal system. The material to be sacrified in this way can be in part water in which case the heat to be absorbed is utilised to cause its vaporisation. Obviously this method is of no advantage unless the weight of material consumed is smaller than that of the fuel which would have been necessary to cause the desired braking effect through retro-rockets.

At the present moment very satisfactory results have been obtained thanks to these various methods in the recovery of rockets whose velocities do not exceed those of artificial satellites, for example, in the case of capsules orbiting the Earth. Such a manoeuvre however does not last more than a few minutes during which the heating effect is considerable ; nevertheless in this short time, the horizontal distance covered by the rocket is more than 2000 km.

Programme for the Future

The sketch which has just been made of the principal problems brought to light by a journey to the Moon has as its principal object that of showing in what direction efforts must still be pursued in order to bring about this century-old dream of mankind. Whilst it is true that these last few years have seen wonders performed, the road still remains barren and a whole series of bridges must still be crossed before this great experiment can be started. Projects under discussion foresee, amongst others, a perilunar journey similar to that of Lunik III but returning to the Earth ; this would permit a close-up photographic study of the Moon under better conditions and the recovery of the film which would then be developed and printed on Earth. As for a landing on the Moon itself, man will not be able to carry this out in person until he has been preceded by numerous robots which would have gathered information on the nature of the surface and particularly on the thickness of the powdery layer, its temperature, intensity of incident radiation... etc. The technique of telecommunication is today so developed that we can reasonably envisage the arrival on the Moon of a rocket provided with all the measuring apparatus desirable, a rocket which would be, for example, provided with caterpillar tracks to enable it to move about and which at predetermined intervals would transmit messages giving an account of the recovered information. Such an experiment is in fact envisaged by the American « Surveyor » programme.

It is quite possible that at the speed at which science progresses today many of these projects will be bypassed before even being carried out but the principles remain and it is only by knowing them thoroughly that one will be able to understand easily how the projects have developed.

PRINTED IN BELGIUM
A S A R — BRUSSELS

la Vierge

le Serpentaire

Maurolyc[...]

Petavius

Frascatorius

MARE
NECTARIS

Catharina

Cyrillus

Langrenus

Theophilus

MARE
FECUNDITATIS

Taruntius

MARE

TRANQUILLITATIS

LE
SCORPION

Antares

MARE
CRISIUM

V[...]

MARE

SERENITATIS

Posidonius

A[...]

le Bouvier

Geminus

Atlas

Hercules

Eudo[...]

Arist[...]

Endymion

COPERNICUS